A Modern Introduction

to

GEOMETRIES

THE UNIVERSITY SERIES IN UNDERGRADUATE MATHEMATICS

Editors

John L. Kelley, *University of California*
Paul R. Halmos, *University of Michigan*

A series of distinguished texts for undergraduate mathematics.
Additional titles will be listed and announced as published.

A Modern Introduction
to
GEOMETRIES

by

ANNITA TULLER

Associate Professor of Mathematics
Hunter College of the City University of New York

D. VAN NOSTRAND COMPANY, INC.
PRINCETON, NEW JERSEY
Toronto   New York   London

D. VAN NOSTRAND COMPANY, INC.
120 Alexander St., Princeton, New Jersey (*Principal office*)
24 West 40 Street, New York 18, New York

D. VAN NOSTRAND COMPANY, LTD.
358 Kensington High Street, London, W.14, England

D. VAN NOSTRAND COMPANY (Canada), LTD.
25 Hollinger Road, Toronto 16, Canada

PRINTED IN THE UNITED STATES OF AMERICA

To

MY HUSBAND

PREFACE

This book has been written in an attempt to aid in the "resetting of geometry in the curriculum" (collected reports of the Committee on the Undergraduate Program of the Mathematical Association of America, 1957), insofar as this can be done in a one-semester course. It was planned in the light of the following statements:

(1) "The unhappy state of geometry in the college curriculum is well known. . . . There was a time when a student had acquired some degree of maturity in geometry by the time he entered a Junior or Senior course in the subject, but this is no longer the case in general." (Report on a Conference on Undergraduate Mathematics Curricula held at Hunter College on October 12–13, 1956.)

(2) "An important consideration in any discussion of curricular revision in mathematics is the availability of teachers able and willing to offer instruction in the subject matter included in the curriculum and to give it in the spirit of contemporary mathematics. . . . It is quite futile to expect the secondary schools to move in the direction of a more modern program if the colleges do not make extensive changes in the spirit and content of their courses." (Commission on Mathematics of the College Entrance Examination Board.)

For centuries after Euclid gave his famous reply to Ptolemy that "there is no royal road to geometry," the only path was by way of Euclid's Elements. Only within recent times has a new route appeared, a broad, modern highway with fascinating byways branching off in many directions. The purpose of this book is to bring to the student an awareness of these new roads and to point out the broad fields to which they lead. Thus Euclidean is shown to be but one geometry among many geometries.

In writing a textbook of this type there is always the problem of selection and organization of material. Great is the temptation to compile a set of one's favorite topics that may be related only by the fact that they are all generally accepted as being "geometrical" in nature. An attempt has been made to avoid this pitfall by selecting the subject matter to illustrate two principal approaches to geometry: (1) the study of a body of theorems deduced from a set of axioms, and (2) the study of the invariant theory of a transformation group. These two approaches are, of course, not mutually exclusive, but represent historical attempts to unify mathematical developments in geometry.

It is generally agreed that the "revolution in geometry," and indeed the opening of the modern era in mathematics, began with the discovery of non-Euclidean geometry. The opening chapter of this book is therefore devoted to a brief examination of Euclid's parallel postulate with the aim of presenting some elementary consequences of its negation and of pointing out the part played by the discovery of non-Euclidean geometry in showing up the need for a more rigorous study of the foundations of geometry.

An axiomatic basis is then given for the real projective plane. Properties are deduced for the introduction of a coordinate system so that an analytic model may be constructed. Thereafter, both analytic and synthetic methods are used freely to develop the properties of projective geometry and its subgeometries, ranging from affine to Euclidean geometry.

In the last two chapters, which are independent of each other, we return to non-Euclidean geometry. The first of these presents Klein's projective models of the hyperbolic and elliptic planes, while the second describes Poincaré's circular inversion models of these planes.

With appropriate modification, depending on student preparation and motivation, the material in this textbook has been presented on three academic levels: undergraduates on the junior-senior level, first-year graduate students in the Teacher Education Program who have had little undergraduate geometry, and secondary school teachers in National Science Foundation Institute Programs.

The author agrees with those English Exchange Professors who have criticized American undergraduate education for its tendency to allow the student to become a "slave to a textbook." This book is, therefore, not a long one. Students are encouraged to present both oral and written expository reports based on the references suggested throughout the text. This type of independent study is a valuable experience for all students.

ACKNOWLEDGMENTS

I take this opportunity to express my gratitude to Professor Louis Weisner for first introducing me to non-Euclidean geometry; to Professor Gustav A. Hedlund for his encouraging comments concerning the course outline on which this book is based; to Professors Howard Levi and Israel Rose for their sympathetic interest and words of encouragement during the writing of the manuscript; and to Professor Melvin Hausner for his careful reading of the manuscript and his helpful suggestions for its improvement.

I am most especially indebted to my former teacher, present colleague and friend of many years standing, Professor Carolyn Eisele, for her continual encouragement and constructive criticisms. Professor Eisele suggested writing the book in the first place and used a mimeographed version in her classes at Hunter College. It is with pleasure that I record here my thanks to her for all the time and energy she spent on this book.

I wish to record my appreciation for the suggestions contributed by my students at Hunter College on whom the material was tried out during the years that it took for the book to grow from a set of lecture notes. It is also a pleasure to acknowledge the assistance of Ida L. Soontup in the typing of several versions of the manuscript.

Finally, I wish to thank my husband, Morris Levine, for his aid in drawing the diagrams and correcting the proofs, and for his patience and understanding during the writing of the manuscript.

ANNITA TULLER

CONTENTS

PART II   Geometry as the Study of the Invariant Theory of a Transformation Group

CHAPTER 4   INTRODUCTION: KLEIN'S *ERLANGER PROGRAMM*   65

CHAPTER 5   LINEAR TRANSFORMATIONS: PROJECTIVE GEOMETRY   71

CHAPTER 6   SUBGEOMETRIES OF PROJECTIVE GEOMETRY   104

PART I

GEOMETRY AS THE STUDY OF A BODY OF THEOREMS DEDUCED FROM A SET OF AXIOMS

CHAPTER 1

INTRODUCTION: NON-EUCLIDEAN GEOMETRY

The discovery of non-Euclidean geometry in the 19th century is generally considered to mark the beginning of modern mathematics, just as the impressionist painting of the same period is considered to mark the beginning of modern art. There was revolution in the air—political revolution, artistic revolution, scientific revolution. The time was ripe for challenging tradition in all fields and mathematics was no exception. In this introductory chapter we shall present a brief account of the early development of non-Euclidean geometry and its impact on philosophy and mathematics.

1.1 Euclid's Elements

The earliest systematic method used in the study of geometry was the deductive axiomatic method introduced by the Greeks. Thales (640–546 B.C.) is generally considered to be the first to treat geometry as a logical structure. In the next 300 years much geometric knowledge was developed. Then Euclid (c. 300 B.C.) collected and systematized all the geometry previously created. He did this by starting out with a set of axioms, statements to be accepted as "true," from which all theorems were deduced as logical consequences.

Though the Greeks realized the need for axioms, they did not seem to find a logical need for undefined terms. Euclid therefore attempted to define everything (Appendix 1). Some of these definitions are meaningless. We now realize that some primitive terms, such as line and point, must remain undefined with their properties given by the axioms, not by intuition.

The assumptions which Euclid used in his proofs were not all stated explicitly. For example, there is nothing in Euclid's axioms from which we can deduce that an angle bisector of a triangle will intersect the opposite side. Then, too, where constructions demand the intersection of two circles, or of a line and a circle, Euclid simply assumed the existence of the needed points of intersection. Though there were attempts to improve on Euclid's definitions and axioms (Heath, P. 155–240*), nevertheless, until the 19th century, Euclid reigned supreme. Then came the discovery of non-Euclidean geometry and with it a re-examination of the foundations of Euclidean geometry.

1.2   The Euclidean Axiom of Parallelism

The first four of Euclid's axioms (Appendix 1) were accepted as simple and "obvious." The fifth, however, was not. Euclid proved his first 28 propositions without using the fifth axiom or postulate (we make no distinction between these terms). For 2000 years mathematicians tried to prove this axiom; i.e., tried to deduce it from the other axioms and the first 28 propositions. But they succeeded only in replacing it by various equivalent assumptions. We present one such "proof" as an example, given by Posidonius in the 1st century B.C. In Fig. 1.21 it is given that

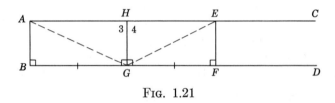

Fig. 1.21

$AB \perp BD$, and $\angle CAB$ is acute. We are to prove that line AC meets line BD. We use the indirect method and assume that $AC \parallel BD$. At any point $F \neq B$ of line BD a perpendicular is erected meeting line AC at E, and GH is erected perpendicular to BD at the midpoint G of BF. Lines AG and GE are then drawn. Since $AC \parallel BD$, then $FE = GH = BA$, and by congruent triangles it is easily shown that $\angle BAC = \angle AEF$. In a similar fashion it is shown that $\angle HAB = \angle 3$, and $\angle HEF = \angle 4$. This leads to the impossible result that $\angle 3$ and $\angle 4$ are acute. Thus the assumption that $AC \parallel BD$ must be rejected and the conclusion reached that AC meets BD. We leave to the student the problem of finding the hidden assumption used in this proof in place of the fifth axiom.

Exercises

1. Show that the following statements are equivalent to Euclid's fifth postulate; i.e., for each statement show first that on the basis of all of Euclid, the statement can be deduced as a theorem; and then that Euclid's fifth postulate can be deduced as a theorem on the basis of his first four postulates, the given statement, and the first 28 propositions. (a) If a line intersects one of two parallel lines it also intersects the other (Proclus, 5th century A.D.). (b) Through a point outside a line only one line can be drawn parallel to the given line (Playfair, 1748–1819).

*For references cited in text, see Bibliography, p. 189.

2. What is the hidden axiom used in the "proof" of Sec. 1.2 in place of Euclid's fifth postulate?

References*

Bonola, Chaps. I and II; Blumenthal, Chap. I; Eves, Chap. I; Eves and Newsom, Chaps. 1 and II; Fishback, Chap. 3; Meserve, Chap. 7; Prenowitz and Jordan, Chap. 2; Wolfe, Chaps. I and II; Yearbook, Chap. IX.

1.3　The Hyperbolic Axiom of Parallelism

In the 19th century the conclusion was reached that not only could the parallel postulate not be proved, but that a logical system of geometry could be constructed without its use. Up to this point no one thought of arguing against the "truth" of Euclid's parallel postulate. But in the 19th century the founders of non-Euclidean geometry—Carl Friedrich Gauss (1777–1855) in Germany, Nicolai Ivanovitch Lobachevsky (1793–1856) in Russia, and Johann Bolyai (1802–1860) in Hungary—concluded independently that a consistent geometry denying Euclid's parallel postulate could be set up. The discovery of non-Euclidean geometry is one of the most thrilling episodes in the history of mathematics. The student is referred to the Bonola reference in the bibliography containing in its appendix the papers of Bolyai and Lobachevsky. The students with a reading knowledge of German will find Gauss' letters on the subject fascinating reading. These may be found in his *Collected Works*, Vol. 8, pp. 159–270. Gauss, from 1792 to 1813, did try to prove Euclid's parallel postulate, but after 1813 his letters show that he had overcome the usual prejudice and developed a non-Euclidean geometry. But, fearing ridicule and controversy, he kept these revolutionary ideas to himself, except for letters to his friends. Lobachevsky and Bolyai were the first to publish expositions of the new geometry, Lobachevsky in 1829 and Bolyai in 1832. Neither created much of an impression in his lifetime. Not until after Gauss' death, when it was learned through his notes and letters that *he*, the Prince of Mathematicians, had considered the material important, did recognition come to the others. Activity then went on in the development of this new geometry and other geometries, as well as in the study of the foundations of mathematics.

Without attempting a rigorous approach we will develop briefly some properties of the first non-Euclidean geometry, known as *Lobachevskian* or *hyperbolic geometry*. This last name was given to the geometry by Felix Klein for reasons that will appear evident in a later chapter. We will make free use of Euclid's axioms (both stated and implied), except the fifth, and of all of Euclid's theorems which do not depend on the fifth postulate;

*For complete reference, see Bibliography, p. 189.

e.g., the first 28 propositions (Appendix 1). Euclid's fifth postulate will be replaced by the following:

Hyperbolic axiom of parallelism: If p is any line and P is a point not on p, then at least two distinct lines can be drawn through P which do not intersect p.

We now adopt a definition of parallel lines more general than that of Euclid. In Fig. 1.31 let Q be the foot of the perpendicular from P to p.

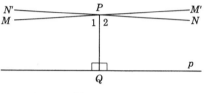

FIG. 1.31

Rotate PQ about P in a counterclockwise direction until PQ no longer intersects p. Euclid's 28th proposition guarantees the existence of such a position. Assume that PN is the first such non-intersecting line. (It is left to the student to prove that there is no last line through P intersecting p.). Let PM be the first non-intersecting line obtained by rotating PQ about P in a clockwise direction. The equality of $\angle 1$ and $\angle 2$, which seems evident by the symmetry of the figure, will be proven later (Theorem 1.41). Now Euclid's axiom of parallelism states essentially that PN and PM are parts of the same line, while the hyperbolic axiom says they are not. The lines PN and PM are said to be *parallel* to p, one in each direction. All other lines through P which do not meet p (those within $\angle NPM'$ or $\angle MPN'$) are said to be *ultra-parallel* to p. In short, the two lines through P which are parallel to p separate the lines which are ultra-parallel to p from those which intersect p; and any line through P meets p if and only if it is within $\angle MPN$. It can be shown that parallelism as thus defined is symmetric; i.e., if $AB \parallel CD$ then $CD \parallel AB$. Also, if two lines are both parallel to a third line in the same direction, then they are parallel to each other.

Exercise

In the above rotation process show that there is no *last* line through P intersecting p.

1.4   Asymptotic Triangles and the Angle of Parallelism

It is convenient to regard all lines parallel to a given line in the same direction as having a common "point at infinity" or *ideal point*. The figure

consisting of two parallel lines cut by a transversal intersecting the lines in
A and B is then regarded as a special kind of triangle $\triangle AB\Omega$ with Ω the
ideal point determined by the given parallels. After Coxeter, we shall call
such a triangle an *asymptotic triangle*. The student is cautioned not to
apply Euclid's triangle theorems to an asymptotic triangle, since this is
not a triangle in the Euclidean sense. The two ideal points on each line,
one in each direction, do not belong to the plane at all.

THEOREM 1.41 *If two asymptotic triangles $AB\Omega$ and $A'B'\Omega'$ have $\angle B =$
$\angle B'$ and $AB = A'B'$, then $\angle A = \angle A'$ (Fig. 1.41).*

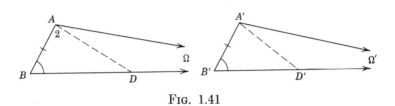

FIG. 1.41

We use the indirect method and assume first that $\angle A > \angle A'$. A line is
then drawn through A as shown in the figure making $\angle 2 = \angle A'$. This
line must intersect $B\Omega$ in a point D. (Why?) On $B'\Omega'$ we lay off $B'D' =$
BD, and draw $A'D'$. Then $\triangle ABD$ is congruent to $\triangle A'B'D'$ and hence
$\angle D'A'B' = \angle 2 = \angle A'$, which is absurd. Therefore $\angle A$ cannot be
greater than $\angle A'$. Similarly we show that $\angle A$ cannot be less than $\angle A'$
and thus conclude that $\angle A = \angle A'$.

Angle of parallelism: From Theorem 1.41 it follows that the two lines
through a point P which are parallel to a line p, make equal angles with the
perpendicular from P to p. Either of these angles is called the *angle of
parallelism* for the perpendicular distance from P to p. We denote this
distance by d and, adopting Lobachevsky's notation, we denote the corresponding angle of parallelism by $\pi(d)$. Theorem 1.41 then implies that
if $d = d'$ then $\pi(d) = \pi(d')$; i.e., angles of parallelism for equal distances
are equal.

THEOREM 1.42 *Angles of parallelism are acute angles.*

Referring back to Fig. 1.31, we see that if $\angle NPQ$ and $\angle MPQ$ were right
angles then MPN would be a straight line. But this contradicts the hyperbolic axiom of parallelism and definition of parallel lines. If $\angle NPQ$ and
$\angle MPQ$ were obtuse, then the line through P perpendicular to PQ would be
within $\angle NPQ$ and hence would meet p. This contradicts Euclid's 28th
proposition. Therefore $\angle NPQ$ and $\angle MPQ$ are acute.

COROLLARY *Two lines which are perpendicular to the same line are ultra-parallel to each other.*

THEOREM 1.43 *In an asymptotic triangle $AB\Omega$ the exterior angle at A is greater than the interior angle at B (Fig. 1.42).*

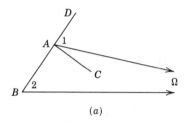
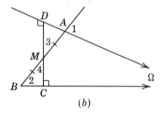

(a)   (b)

FIG. 1.42

We assume first that $\measuredangle 1 < \measuredangle 2$ [Fig. 1.42(a)]. Then draw AC to make $\measuredangle DAC = \measuredangle 2$. But AC intersects $B\Omega$ (Why?) forming a triangle with an exterior angle ($\measuredangle CAD$) equal to a remote interior angle ($\measuredangle 2$). This contradicts Euclid's 16th proposition. We then assume that $\measuredangle 1 = \measuredangle 2$ [Fig. 1.42(b)]. From M, the midpoint of AB, draw MC and MD perpendicular to $B\Omega$ and $A\Omega$, respectively. By showing that $\triangle ADM$ is congruent to $\triangle BCM$ and hence that $\measuredangle 3 = \measuredangle 4$, we can then show that DMC is a straight line. Therefore $D\Omega$ and $B\Omega$ are both perpendicular to DC and hence are ultraparallel, contrary to the hypothesis. Hence $\measuredangle 1 > \measuredangle 2$.

COROLLARY *The angle of parallelism decreases as the distance increases; i.e., if $d > d'$ then $\pi(d) < \pi(d')$.*

We note that as d tends to zero, $\pi(d)$ approaches a right angle; so that for "small" distances hyperbolic geometry is "close" to Euclidean geometry.

THEOREM 1.44 *If two asymptotic triangles $AB\Omega$ and $A'B'\Omega'$ have $\measuredangle A = \measuredangle A'$ and $\measuredangle B = \measuredangle B'$, then $AB = A'B'$ (Fig. 1.43).*

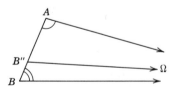
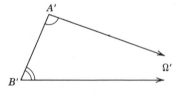

FIG. 1.43

Assume $AB > A'B'$ and on AB lay off $AB'' = A'B'$. Draw $B''\Omega$; i.e., through B'' draw the line parallel to $B\Omega$. Then $\angle AB''\Omega > \angle B$ by Theorem 1.43. But $\angle B = \angle B'$ by hypothesis, and $\angle B' = \angle AB''\Omega$ by Theorem 1.41. Hence $\angle AB''\Omega > \angle AB''\Omega$ which is absurd. In a similar fashion we see that AB cannot be less than $A'B'$. Hence $AB = A'B'$.

COROLLARY 1   *If $\pi(d) = \pi(d')$ then $d = d'$.*

COROLLARY 2   *If $\pi(d) > \pi(d')$ then $d < d'$.*

Note: The preceding theorems and corollaries establish a functional relationship between a distance d and an angle $\pi(d)$. Now in both Euclidean and hyperbolic geometry an angle can be measured in terms of a unit which can be constructed at will; e.g., a right angle may be the chosen unit. In Euclidean geometry a unit of length, however, has to be arbitrarily set and preserved in some central place like the Bureau of Standards. But in hyperbolic geometry the unit of length can be determined by the unit of angle. For example, we can say that the unit of length shall be the distance d for which $\pi(d)$ is half a right angle. Thus we say that in hyperbolic geometry there exists an *absolute unit of length* as well as an absolute unit of angle measure.

Exercises

1. Prove the corollaries to Theorems 1.42, 1.43, 1.44.

2. If in asymptotic triangle $AB\Omega$, $\angle A = \angle B$, prove that the line through the midpoint of AB which is parallel to $A\Omega$ and $B\Omega$ is perpendicular to AB and that any point on that line is equidistant from $A\Omega$ and $B\Omega$.

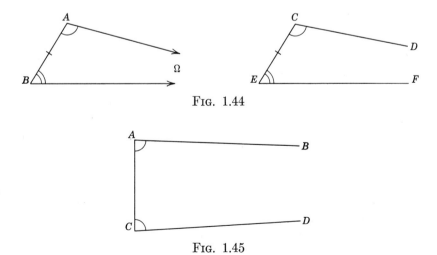

FIG. 1.44

FIG. 1.45

3. If in asymptotic triangle $AB\Omega$, $\angle A = \angle B$, prove that the perpendicular bisector of AB is parallel to $A\Omega$ and $B\Omega$.

4. Prove the converse of Exercise 3.

5. If in Fig. 1.44, $A\Omega \parallel B\Omega$, $\angle A = \angle C$, $\angle B = \angle E$ and $AB = CE$, prove that $CD \parallel EF$.

6. If in Fig. 1.45, AB and CD are ultra-parallel and if $\angle A = \angle C$, prove that the perpendicular bisector of AC is ultraparallel to both AB and CD.

1.5   The Saccheri Quadrilateral

Another figure which plays an important role in the development of hyperbolic geometry is the *Saccheri quadrilateral*, named for Gerolamo Saccheri (1667–1733) who used it in his attempt to prove Euclid's parallel postulate. This is a quadrilateral (Fig. 1.51) $ABCD$ with two adjacent

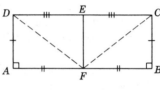

Fig. 1.51

right angles at A and B and with sides $AD = BC$. The line AB joining the vertices of the right angles is called the *base* and its opposite side DC is called the *summit* of the quadrilateral.

Theorem 1.51   *In a Saccheri quadrilateral the line joining the midpoints of the base and summit is perpendicular to both, and the summit angles are equal* (Fig. 1.51).

Details of the proof are left to the student. Draw the lines indicated in Fig. 1.51 and use congruent triangles. Note that this theorem holds in Euclidean geometry too.

Corollary   *The base and summit of a Saccheri quadrilateral are ultraparallel.*

Theorem 1.52   *The summit angles of a Saccheri quadrilateral are acute* (Fig. 1.52).

Draw $D\Omega$ and $C\Omega$ parallel to AB. (Why will they fall within the angles EDA and ECB, respectively?) Now $\angle 4 = \angle 1$ and $\angle 5 > \angle 2$. (Why?) Hence $\angle 4 + \angle 5 > \angle 1 + \angle 2$. But $\angle 1 + \angle 2 = \angle 3$. (Why?) Hence $\angle BCE > \angle 3$, and $\angle 3$ is acute.

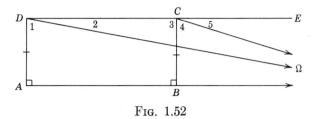

FIG. 1.52

Historical Note: Saccheri, after setting up the quadrilateral and proving that the summit angles are equal, considered three possibilities: that the summit angles are obtuse, or right, or acute. These possibilities are known historically as "the hypothesis of the obtuse angle, the hypothesis of the right angle, and the hypothesis of the acute angle." He intended to establish Euclid's parallel postulate by showing that the first and third hypotheses lead to contradictions and that the second hypothesis implies Euclid's fifth postulate. In his unsuccessful attempt to find contradictions in the hypothesis of the acute angle, he discovered many theorems of what is now known as hyperbolic geometry.

THEOREM 1.53   *The sum of the angles of a triangle is less than a straight angle* (Fig. 1.53).

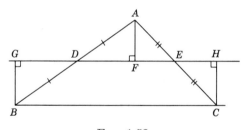

FIG. 1.53

Let E and D be the midpoints of sides AC and AB of $\triangle ABC$. AF, BG, and CH are perpendiculars drawn from the vertices of the given triangle to the line determined by D and E. Then triangles BGD and AFD are congruent, as are also triangles CHE and AFE. Thus $BG = AF = CH$ and $GHCB$ is a Saccheri quadrilateral, whose summit angles GBC and BCH are acute. From the congruent triangles it is seen that the sum of the angles of the triangle is equal to the sum of the summit angles of the Saccheri quadrilateral. Hence the theorem follows.

DEFINITION 1.51   The amount by which the sum of the angles of a triangle differs from a straight angle is called the *defect* of the triangle.

COROLLARY 1   *The sum of the angles of a quadrilateral is less than two straight angles.*

COROLLARY 2   *Two lines cannot have more than one common perpendicular.*

THEOREM 1.54   *If three angles of one triangle are equal respectively to three angles of the second triangle, then the two triangles are congruent* (Fig. 1.54).

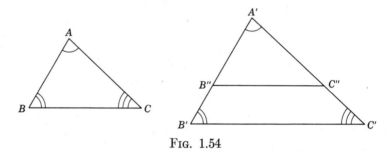

FIG. 1.54

Assume $AB < A'B'$ and on $A'B'$ lay off $A'B'' = AB$, and draw $\sphericalangle A'B''C'' = \sphericalangle ABC$. Then triangles ABC and $A'B''C''$ are congruent and $\sphericalangle A'C''B'' = \sphericalangle C = \sphericalangle C'$. But this makes the sum of the angles of quadrilateral $B'B''C''C'$ equal to two straight angles, which is impossible. Similarly we see that AB cannot be greater than $A'B'$. Hence $AB = A'B'$ and $\triangle ABC$ is congruent to $\triangle A'B'C'$.

THEOREM 1.55   *The perpendicular distance from a point on one of two parallel lines to the other decreases as the point moves in the direction of parallelism* (Fig. 1.55).

In quadrilateral $ABDC$ there are right angles at B and D. Therefore $\sphericalangle 2 + \sphericalangle 3 < \pi$, while $\sphericalangle 1 + \sphericalangle 3 = \pi$. Hence $\sphericalangle 1 > \sphericalangle 2$, making $CD < AB$. (Why?) (This theorem reveals the hidden axiom used in the "proof" given in Sec. 1.2.)

Since parallel lines are *not* everywhere equidistant, what *is* the locus of points equidistant from a given line? Consider Fig. 1.56 where A, B, C

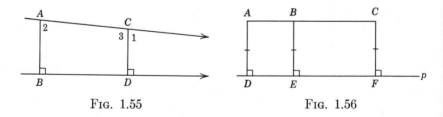

FIG. 1.55   FIG. 1.56

are points equidistant from line p. Draw lines AB and BC. Two Saccheri quadrilaterals are formed whose summit angles are therefore acute. Hence ABC is not a straight line. The required locus is a curve called an *equidistant curve* or *hypercycle*. It has two branches, one on each side of the given line. The given line is called the *base line*.

To the student whose answer to the question of the preceding paragraph was "an ultra-parallel," we state that it can be shown that two ultra-parallel lines have a unique common perpendicular, that this perpendicular is the shortest distance between them, and that the perpendicular distance from a point on one to the other increases as the point moves away from the common perpendicular in either direction (see Wolfe, Chap. IV).

With the help of the Saccheri quadrilateral it can be shown that two triangles having the same angle sum are equal in area and conversely. As a result of this and Exercise 6 at the end of this section, it can be shown that the area of a triangle is proportional to its defect; i.e.,

$$\text{area } \Delta ABC = k^2(\pi - A - B - C).$$

From this it follows that the area of a triangle increases as the sum of its angles decreases, and has a finite upper bound of $k^2\pi$.

Exercises

1. Prove Theorem 1.51 and its corollary.

2. Prove the corollaries of Theorem 1.53.

3. Show that the sum of the angles of a convex polygon of n sides is less than $(n - 2)$ straight angles.

4. Show that an angle inscribed in a semicircle is an acute angle.

5. Show that if the sum of the angles of a triangle is the same for all triangles, then that sum is π. Hence, in the hyperbolic plane, the sum of the angles of a triangle cannot be the same for all triangles.

6. If a triangle is divided into two triangles by a line from a vertex to a point on the opposite side, show that the defect of the triangle is equal to the sum of the defects of the two smaller triangles.

7. Prove that the line joining any point on one branch of a hypercycle to any point on the other branch is bisected by the base line.

8. Prove that if a quadrilateral is inscribed in one branch of a hypercycle, the sum of one pair of opposite angles is equal to the sum of the other pair.

9. State and prove theorems analogous to that of the previous exercise for the case where two vertices of the quadrilateral are on one branch and two on the other, and for the case where three vertices are on one branch and one on the other.

10. A regular network of regular n-sided polygons is to be constructed in the hyperbolic plane, p of which meet at a point. Show that the area of each polygon is $\pi k^2(n - 2 - 2n/p)$, where $1/n + 1/p < 1/2$. Show also that the area of the smallest finite regular quadrilateral with which the plane could be paved is $2/5(\pi k^2)$.

References

Adler, Chap. 14; Bonola, Chaps. III and IV; Coxeter (2), Chap. 14; Eves, Chap. VII; Eves and Newsom, Chap. III; Moise, Chap. 24; Prenowitz & Jordan, Chap. 4; Wolfe, Chaps. III and IV; Young, J.W.A., Chap. III.

1.6   The Elliptic Axiom of Parallelism

There remains now the question of the possibility of replacing Euclid's fifth postulate by one denying the existence of any parallel lines. Such an assumption, however, contradicts Euclid's 27th proposition which guarantees the existence of at least one parallel to a given line through a point not on the given line. This proposition was proven without the use of any parallel postulate. Its proof depends on the 16th proposition: An exterior angle of a triangle is greater than either interior opposite angle. The proof of this theorem is of sufficient importance to be reproduced here and discussed in some detail (Fig. 1.61).* We are to prove that $\angle BCE > \angle B$.

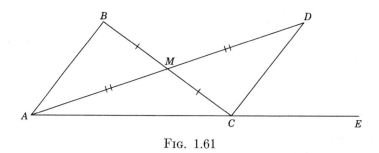

FIG. 1.61

The median AM is extended its own length to D and line DC is drawn. $\triangle ABM$ is then seen to be congruent to $\triangle DCM$ and hence $\angle B = \angle BCD$. Therefore $\angle BCE > \angle B$.

We now note a significant flaw in Euclid's proof of the above theorem. How do we know where point D will fall? *Must* it fall within $\angle BCE$? Perhaps AM, when extended, intersects AE, and D falls on AE or on the other side of AE. This would make $\angle BCD \geq \angle BCE$ and the theorem would not hold. Or perhaps line AM, when extended, comes back upon itself so that D falls on the backward extension of AM. In short, Euclid tacitly assumed that his first postulate implied that two straight lines cannot enclose an area, and that his second postulate implied that a straight line is infinite in length.

Bernhard Riemann (1826–1866), in a lecture delivered in 1854, pointed out the importance of distinguishing between *unboundedness* and *infinitude*

---

*Reprinted from Sir Thomas Heath, *The Thirteen Books of Euclid's Elements*, by permission of the Cambridge University Press.

in connection with concepts of space. He showed that it was possible to have a geometry in which a line is boundless but not infinite; i.e., it has no "ends" but it may come back on itself and thus have a finite length.

For this new geometry, therefore, we explicitly postulate that *every straight line is boundless.* We then replace Euclid's fifth postulate by the following:

Elliptic axiom of parallelism: Two lines in a plane always intersect.

We note that we can no longer accept the first 28 propositions of Euclid as we did for hyperbolic geometry. Any propositions which depend on the infinitude of a line, such as the 16th and its consequences, are not in general valid in elliptic geometry. Here we begin to see the need for a more careful formulation of the axiomatic basis of Euclidean geometry as well as the non-Euclidean geometries. This problem will be considered in the next chapter. Now, however, we stress the fact that if we accept *all* of Euclid's axioms, expressed and implied, and then try to replace his axiom of parallelism by the elliptic axiom of parallelism, we arrive at a contradiction. The set of axioms is then termed *inconsistent* and a geometry cannot be built on it. Mathematicians before Riemann therefore rejected this axiom of parallelism (or its equivalent). Riemann suggested rejecting the infinitude of the line instead, thereby opening the way for a new *Riemannian* or *elliptic* geometry.

It is not our intention here to develop the properties of elliptic geometry. For purposes of comparison with Euclidean and hyperbolic geometry, however, we state some theorems without proof and refer the student to the references at the end of this section for details.

THEOREM 1.61   *All lines perpendicular to the same line p meet in a point P, at a constant distance q from p. The point P is called the* pole *of line p, and p is called the* polar *of P.*

THEOREM 1.62   *The distance q from a line to its pole is the same for all lines. The polar p of a given point P is the set of points whose distance from P is q.*

THEOREM 1.63   *Every line through a point P is perpendicular to the polar of P.*

THEOREM 1.64   *All straight lines have the same finite length. A line is reentrant; i.e., if we start from a point A and traverse the line in either direction, we return to A.*

THEOREM 1.65   *All lines which pass through a point P meet again in a point P' such that PP' = 2q. Thus a line may have two poles.*

Corollary 1   *Two lines in the elliptic plane enclose an area.*

Corollary 2   *Two points determine a line provided that the two points are not poles of the same line; i.e., provided that the distance between the two points is less than 2q.*

Theorem 1.66   *In a Saccheri quadrilateral the summit angles are equal and obtuse.*

Theorem 1.67   *The sum of the angles of a triangle is greater than a straight angle.*

Theorem 1.68   *If the three angles of one triangle are equal respectively to the three angles of another, the triangles are congruent.*

Theorem 1.69   *The area of a triangle is proportional to its excess; i.e., area $\triangle ABC = k^2(A + B + C - \pi)$.*

As a result of Theorem 1.65 we have two geometries, distinguished by the assumptions that P and P' are distinct or that they coincide. The first is called *double elliptic* or *spherical* geometry. If we consider the surface of a Euclidean sphere and define a straight line as a great circle of this sphere, we can show that the double elliptic geometry of the plane is identical with the geometry on the surface of the sphere. The k in Theorem 1.69 is the radius of the sphere. The student will have no difficulty verifying the above theorems on the surface of the sphere. Thus the theorems of this non-Euclidean geometry were well known at the time of Euclid. This geometry is of interest to us here because of the fact that its properties were shown to be derivable without recourse to Euclidean space.

The second of the two elliptic geometries is called *single elliptic* or simply *elliptic geometry.* In this geometry two lines have only one point in common but still enclose an area; and two distinct points always determine a line. Felix Klein (1849–1925) pointed out the close relationship between the single elliptic plane and the real projective plane which will be discussed later.

Exercises

1. If the locus of points a fixed distance from a fixed point is called a *circle,* discuss the existence of circles for different fixed distances. Also discuss the existence of the locus of points a fixed distance from a given line. (Use the spherical model. The same problem for the single elliptic plane is more difficult but may be studied by using as a model a hemisphere with diametrically opposite points on its boundary considered as coincident.)

2. Why is Euclid's 16th proposition not necessarily valid in elliptic geometry?

References

Adler, Chap. 15; Prenowitz and Jordan, Chap. 4; Wolfe, pp. 173–181; Young, J.W.A., pp. 106–115.

1.7   Significance of the Discovery of Non-Euclidean Geometry

In addition to settling the parallel postulate controversy, the discovery of the non-Euclidean geometries of Gauss, Bolyai, Lobachevsky and Riemann opened the way for the creation of other geometries. Speculation arose, for example, concerning geometries that might result from changing other Euclidean axioms, or even by starting out with completely new sets of axioms. Then too, Riemann's lecture of 1854, which served as the starting point for elliptic geometry, used a method which created at once an infinite number of geometries, and extended the results to spaces of any number of dimensions.

The discovery of the non-Euclidean geometries also brought about a revolution in philosophic thought. It gave new significance to the whole question of the nature of truth. Before this the postulates of Euclid were viewed as absolute truths, not as mere assumptions no more "true" than other assumptions which might contradict them. The question "Which is the *true* geometry?" is now recognized as having no meaning. All we can say about the truth of a geometry, considered as a mathematical system, is that if the postulates are true then the theorems are true.

The question assumes a different aspect when geometry is considered as a description of the physical universe. Then it is a question of which geometry agrees with experimental evidence. We noted (Cor. to Th. 1.43) that for "small" distances hyperbolic geometry is close to Euclidean geometry. Gauss, therefore, tried to answer the question by measuring the sum of the angles of a triangle formed by three mountain peaks. The difference between the measured sum and 180° was no greater than could be accounted for by the necessary allowance for experimental error. Lobachevsky worked with astronomical distances with similar results. At the beginning of the 20th century, however, Henri Poincaré (1854–1912) pointed out that the physical experimenter must start with some assumptions just as the mathematician does, and that it was therefore impossible to determine the geometry of space by physical experiment. Let us suppose, for example, that the sum of the angles of an astronomical triangle was indeed found to be significantly less than 180°. This may be explained by saying that space is hyperbolic. It may also be accounted for by saying that space is Euclidean but that the light rays forming the sides of the triangle curved inward instead of being straight. There is no way of deciding whether to keep the mathematical or the physical axiom.

For applications to the physical world we choose the mathematical system which is most convenient. For example, Einstein in his study of relativity adopted one of the set of Riemannian geometries mentioned above. More recently, hyperbolic geometry was used to describe space as observed by people of normal vision; e.g., parallel lines behave visually as described by Theorem 1.55. Figure 1.71 illustrates an experiment reported in the March

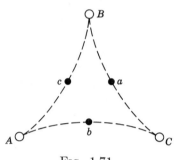

FIG. 1.71

9, 1962 issue of *Science*. Subjects were asked to place light sources a, b, c at what they perceived to be the midpoints of the sides of a triangle formed by three fixed light sources A, B, C, in a horizontal plane at eye level. The results generally indicated triangles with sides that curved inward, affording further evidence that binocular visual space might well be described by hyperbolic geometry.

The study of the independence of Euclid's parallel postulate and the discovery of non-Euclidean geometry led also to a critical study of the foundations of Euclidean geometry and of the nature of axiom systems in general. The geometric road was found to be badly in need of additions and repairs. Its foundations were shaky, the pavement had cracks and there was definite need for expansion. In the next chapter we will see how new foundations were laid. Then we will follow some new roads and look at some of the additions of the past 150 years.

Further References for Chapter 1

Barker, S. F., *Philosophy of Mathematics* (Prentice-Hall, Inc., Englewood Cliffs, New Jersey, 1964).

Luneberg, R. K., *Mathematical Analysis of Binocular Vision* (Princeton University Press, Princeton, New Jersey, 1947).

Poincarè, H., *Science and Hypothesis* (Dover Publications, Inc., New York, 1952).

CHAPTER 2

AXIOM SYSTEMS

2.1 Defects in Euclid

In the preceding chapter some of the logical gaps in Euclid's Elements were pointed out; e.g., the inadequacy of his definitions and his use of hidden assumptions. We wish here to mention a few more before discussing other postulate systems for Euclidean geometry.

First there is Euclid's use of superposition; i.e., motion without deformation, where one triangle is placed upon another to prove congruence. That the right to do this must be explicity stated is seen by trying to do this on the surface of an egg.

Then there is Euclid's reliance on intuition in drawing figures for his proofs. For example, in the proofs for standard constructions it is assumed that certain circles intersect, and that a line joining a point inside a circle to a point outside the circle must intersect the circle. The need for some kind of continuity axiom for the Euclidean plane is seen by noting that if we consider the plane as consisting only of those points whose rectangular coordinates are rational numbers, then the line $y = x$ does *not* intersect the circle $x^2 + y^2 = 1$, even though it joins the point (0,0) inside the circle to the point (1,1) outside the circle.

Then there is the "intuition" involved in assuming that the bisector of an angle of a triangle intersects the opposite side, or that a line intersecting one side of a triangle must intersect one or both of the other two sides. For these we need an axiom to account for the two "sides" of a line, the "interior" of an angle or triangle, etc.

To point up the danger in relying on figures in proofs we present two classic examples:

Example 1: "Proof" that every triangle is isosceles: The bisector of $\sphericalangle A$ meets the perpendicular bisector of BC at D. From D perpendiculars are drawn to AB and AC and lines to each vertex as shown in Fig. 2.11. $\triangle ADF \cong \triangle ADE$, and $\triangle BDG \cong \triangle CDG$. Then $\triangle BDF \cong \triangle CDE$, and by adding corresponding parts it follows that $AB = AC$.

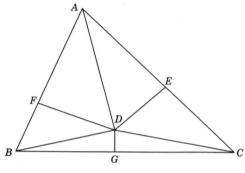

Fig. 2.11

Example 2: "Proof" that there are two perpendiculars from a point to a line: Let any two circles intersect in points A and B. Draw diameters AC and AD as shown in Fig. 2.12 and draw line CD. Let CD intersect the two circles in M and N and draw AM and AN. Then $\angle AMD$ is a right angle as is $\angle ANC$.

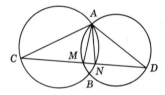

Fig. 2.12

It is left to the student to find the flaws in these proofs. (See Exs. 13 and 14 at the end of Sec. 2.3.)

2.2   Foundations of Euclidean Geometry

Though defects in Euclid's logical structure were pointed out earlier, it was not until after the discovery of non-Euclidean geometry that mathematicians began carefully scrutinizing the foundations of Euclidean geometry and formulating precise sets of axioms for it. The problem was to erect the entire structure of Euclidean geometry upon the simplest foundation possible; i.e., to choose a minimum number of undefined elements and relations and a set of axioms concerning them, with the property that all of Euclidean geometry can be logically deduced from these without any further appeal to intuition. There were many such axiom sets formulated at the end of the 19th century beginning with the work of Pasch (1882), Peano (1889) and Pieri (1899) and culminating with the famous set by Hilbert (1899). New sets were formulated in the 20th century by Veblen

(1904), Forder (1927), Birkhoff (1932), Robinson (1940), Levi (1960) and others. Modifications of these sets are now being used in texts for the new mathematics curricula for secondary schools; e.g., the texts of the School Mathematics Study Group (SMSG).

We here consider briefly postulate systems of Hilbert, Birkhoff, and the SMSG; Hilbert's because it is most closely related to Euclid's and because of its great influence in convincing mathematicians of the importance of the postulational method in all branches of mathematics; Birkhoff's because of its use of the real number system and because of recent interest in it by groups working to improve the teaching and content of secondary school geometry courses; and the SMSG set because it combines Hilbert's and Birkhoff's and is now being used widely in experimental classes.

2.3 Hilbert's Axioms for Euclidean Plane Geometry

Hilbert's axiom set of 1899 was revised in the light of discussion and criticism which followed its appearance. Appendix 2 contains the version published in 1962 in the ninth edition of Hilbert's *Grundlagen der Geometrie* (Foundations of Geometry). The undefined terms are point, line, plane, on, between, and congruent. The set is divided into five groups: incidence, order, congruence, parallelism, and continuity. A comparison of the first three axioms, which follow,

1. Through any two distinct points A, B, there is always a line m.
2. Through any two distinct points A, B, there is not more than one line m.
3. There exist at least three points not on the same line.

with Euclid's first postulate, "To draw a straight line from any point to any point," will serve to point up the defect in Euclid. The new axioms not only explicitly specify the *uniqueness* of the line joining two distinct points but also postulate the *existence* of at least two distinct points to begin with. Nothing is to be taken as intuitively evident. The axioms of congruence eliminate the problem of the use of superposition.

The most important innovation is the set of axioms of order or "betweenness." The symbol (ABC) is often used to denote that point B is between A and C, so that Axiom II–1, for example, may be written: "If (ABC), then A, B, C are distinct points on the same line and (CBA)." We note that Axiom II–2 leads to the existence of an infinite number of points on a line. The first edition of Hilbert's *Foundations* included, as part of Axiom II–2, the statement that, for any two distinct points A and B, there is at least one point C such that (ACB). This was later shown to follow from the other axioms as given in Appendix 2. The student should try to prove this.

As noted in Appendix 2, Pasch's axiom may be replaced by the separation axiom. To show that Pasch's axiom then follows as a theorem we proceed as follows: We are given a line m intersecting side AB of triangle ABC and not passing through a vertex of the triangle (Fig. 2.31). Therefore, by

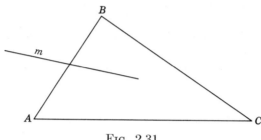

Fig. 2.31

the separation postulate, A and B are on opposite sides of m. Hence C must be on the same side of m as either A or B, but not both. If C is on the A-side of m, then C and B are on opposite sides of m, and hence m intersects side BC. If C is on the B-side of m, then m intersects side AC. Thus Pasch's axiom is shown to be a logical consequence of Hilbert's axioms when Pasch's axiom is relpaced by the separation axiom. To complete the proof of the equivalence of the two axioms, the student should show that the separation axiom is a logical consequence of Hilbert's axiom set.

We are now able to correct the defect mentioned in the proof of the exterior angle theorem (see Sec. 1.6). We define the *interior of triangle ABC* as the intersection of the following three sets of points: the A-side of line BC, the B-side of line AC, and the C-side of line AB. We define the *interior of angle BAC* as the intersection of the set of points on the C-side of line AB with the set of points on the B-side of AC. The exterior angle at C is defined as the angle BCE where E is a point such that (ACE). It is now left to the student to show that point D in Fig. 1.61 lies in the interior of angle BCE.

As noted in Appendix 2, Hilbert's axioms of continuity may be replaced by the axiom of Dedekind. (For a discussion of equivalence, see Kutuzov, p. 542.) To see how this postulate is used to prove that a line joining a point inside a circle to a point outside the circle must intersect the circle, the student is referred to Heath, p. 237.

We close this brief description of Hilbert's axiom set by noting that if the parallel axiom of Group IV is replaced by the hyperbolic axiom of parallelism of Sec. 1.3, an axiomatic basis for hyperbolic geometry is obtained. The basis for elliptic geometry is not so easily obtained from the Euclidean set. For one possible treatment we refer the reader to "An Introduction to

Elliptic Geometry" by David Gans, in the *American Mathematical Monthly*, Vol. 62, No. 7, Part II, 1955.

Exercises

On the basis of Hilbert's axiom set prove:

1. Two lines cannot intersect in more than one point.

2. Through each point there exist at least two distinct lines.

3. Not all lines pass through the same point.

4. For any two distinct points A, B, there is always at least one point C such that (ACB).

5. If two lines are parallel to a third line they are parallel to each other.

6. If two sides and the included angle of one triangle are congruent to two sides and the included angle of another triangle then the remaining side of the first triangle is congruent to the remaining side of the second.

7. If two angles and the included side of one triangle are congruent to two angles and the included side of another triangle then the remaining parts of the first triangle are congruent respectively to the corresponding parts of the second.

8. Complete the proof of the equivalence of Pasch's axiom and the separation axiom.

9. A line through the vertex of a triangle, which contains points inside the triangle, intersects the opposite side.

10. Point D of Fig. 1.61 lies in the interior of angle BCE.

11. A line intersecting one side of a quadrilateral and not going through a vertex must intersect a second side.

12. A line not through a vertex of a triangle cannot intersect all three sides of the triangle.

13. Assuming that all of Euclid's theorems have been proven, show that for a non-isosceles triangle ABC, the bisector of angle A and the perpendicular bisector of side BC meet at a point D on the circumcircle of the triangle; and (using notation in Fig. 2.11) for the two perpendiculars DF and DE the order of points must be (AFB) and (ACE) *or* (ABF) and (AEC).

14. In Fig. 2.12 prove that C, B, D are collinear, thus showing that line CD cannot intersect the two circles in two distinct points.

2.4 Birkhoff's Postulates for Euclidean Plane Geometry

While Hilbert's postulate set is closely related to Euclid's, Birkhoff's represents a very different point of view. By assuming the fundamental properties of real numbers, Birkhoff was able to reduce his postulate system to only four postulates (Appendix 3). His key concepts are *distance* and *similarity*, on which are based the concepts of betweenness, congruence, and parallelism. Birkhoff's postulates were modified and incorporated into a text for secondary school students in 1940. This was too radical a departure from Euclid to gain favor at the time. We mention it here because of the bridge it affords from Hilbert's treatment to that of the SMSG, and also because it points up the fact that the *same* geometry can be developed from such very different postulate systems. We present here just one proof, that of Euclid's parallel postulate which follows as a theorem from Birkhoff's postulates* (Fig. 2.41): Given point P and line p not containing P. Q is

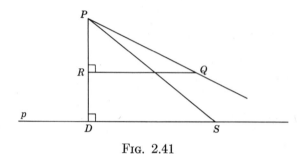

FIG. 2.41

any point such that the line QP makes an acute angle with the perpendicular PD drawn from P to p. We wish to show that line PQ meets p. Draw line QR perpendicular to PD. Let S be a point on p such that DS satisfies the condition $PR : RQ = PD : DS$. Draw line PS. Then $\triangle PRQ$ is similar to $\triangle PDS$ (Post. IV) and hence $\sphericalangle RPQ = \sphericalangle DPS$. Then line PQ coincides with line PS and therefore intersects p.

2.5   The SMSG Postulates for Euclidean Geometry

As we look over this set of postulates (Appendix 4) we note that it combines the ideas of Hilbert and Birkhoff in a form simple enough for use on the secondary school level and gives a basis for the early introduction of analytic methods. In addition there is emphasis on the precise use of symbols and definitions; e.g., a careful distinction is made between *equality* and *congruence*, between a *line segment* (a set of points) and its *length* (a real number), between an *angle* (a set of points) and its *measure* (a real number). The need for such care is brought out in the following illustration:

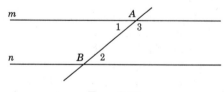

FIG. 2.51

Given: $m \parallel n$, with transversal AB.
Prove: $\sphericalangle 2$ and $\sphericalangle 3$ are supplementary angles.

*Taken from G. D. Birkhoff, "A Set of Postulates for Plane Geometry," *Annals of Mathematics* (V. 33, 1932). With permission from the *Annals of Mathematics*.

1. $m \parallel n$ 1. Given
2. $\angle 1 = \angle 2$ 2. Alternate interior angles
3. $\angle 1$ and $\angle 3$ are supplementary.   3. Definition
4. $\angle 2$ and $\angle 3$ are supplementary.   4. Substitution

Proofs like the above, though not as elegant as one might wish, have nevertheless been considered acceptable. To convince the student of the inadequacy of this proof we present the following*:

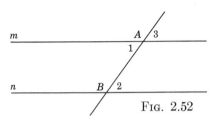

FIG. 2.52

Given: $m \parallel n$, with transversal AB.
Prove: $\angle 2$ and $\angle 3$ are vertical angles.

1. $m \parallel n$ 1. Given
2. $\angle 1 = \angle 2$ 2. Alternate interior angles
3. $\angle 1$ and $\angle 3$ are vertical angles   3. Definition
4. $\angle 2$ and $\angle 3$ are vertical angles   4. Substitution

If the first proof is acceptable then the second is also. But the second is obviously not acceptable. Therefore the first is not acceptable. What went wrong? There was no distinction made between an angle and its measure. In step 3 the angles are used as sets of points; in step 2 the equality refers to the *measures* of the angles (real numbers). Step 2 should read "$m(\angle 1) = m(\angle 2)$." In step 4, therefore, the attempt is being made to substitute a number for a set of points, which of course is not substituting a quantity for its *equal*. (For a more sophisticated example of false reasoning due to the lack of distinction between a set of segments and their lengths, see Ya. S. Dubnov, *Mistakes in Geometric Proofs* (D. C. Heath, 1963, p. 40).

In order to avoid ambiguity SMSG uses the word *equal* to mean "alike in all respects," "identical," or "the same as." Words like "congruent" are carefully defined and care is taken to use these words properly. Two line segments are said to be *congruent* if their *lengths are equal;* two angles are said to be *congruent* if their *measures are equal.* Hence if $d(A, B) = d(A', B')$ and if $d(C, D) = d(C', D')$, it follows that $d(A, B) + d(C, D) = d(A', B') + d(C', D')$; but it does not necessarily follow that the union of segments AB and CD is *congruent* to the union of segments $A'B'$ and $C'D'$, even though

*Reprinted by permission of the publishers from Max Beberman, *An Emerging Program of Secondary School Mathematics* (Harvard University Press, Copyright 1958 by the President and Fellows of Harvard College, Cambridge, Massachusetts).

$AB \cong A'B'$ and $CD \cong C'D'$. The equality involves the algebra of real numbers; the congruence involves the algebra of sets (Fig. 2.53).

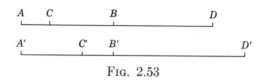

FIG. 2.53

It is not our intention to delve further into the problem of the axiomatic foundation of Euclidean geometry. For details on the development of Euclidean geometry on the basis of the above sets of axioms the student is referred to the references below.

References

Adler, Chap. 2; Eves, Chap. VIII; Fishback, Chaps. 1, 2; Forder; Heath, Book I; Hilbert; Klein, pp. 188–208; Kutuzov, Chap. XII; Levi; Moise; Prenowitz and Jordan, Chap. 1; Robinson; SMSG publications; Young (1), Chaps. I, XIII, XIV, XV; Young, J. W. A., Chap. I.

2.6   Abstract Axiom Systems

From the critical study of the foundations of Euclidean geometry we are led to the consideration of the postulational method in general and its importance in all branches of mathematics. Indeed, going deeper into foundations, mathematicians and philosophers investigated the nature of an abstract deductive science and of the logic used in its development. We shall not elaborate on the latter but shall simply assume the laws of ordinary classical logic.

An abstract deductive science is constructed by choosing an axiom system; i.e., a set of undefined terms and a set of axioms containing them. The science is then developed by deducing theorems from these axioms or from previously deduced theorems by means of the chosen logic. The axiom system as such is meaningless and the question of the "truth" of the axioms is irrelevant. If we can assign meanings to the undefined terms in such a way that the axioms are judged to be "true," we say we have a *model* of the abstract axiom system. Then all theorems deduced from the axiom system are "true" in the sense of the accepted model.

For example, consider a set of undefined elements $a, b, c, \cdots$ and an undefined binary relation R satisfying the following:

Axiom 1: If aRb, then $a \neq b$.

Axiom 2: If aRb and bRc, then aRc.

As a model of this abstract system we may let the undefined elements be positive integers and let aRb mean "a is less than b." As another model we may let the elements be people and let aRb mean "a is an ancestor of b." The student should verify the fact that these are models of the system and should try to think of others.

May *any* arbitrary set of statements serve as a basis for an axiom system? The answer is *No*. A fundamental property which an axiom system must possess is consistency. There are other properties which are not as essential but are sometimes desirable. We shall now consider these properties.

2.7   Consistency of an Axiom System

A set of axioms is said to be *consistent* if it is not possible to deduce from these axioms a theorem which contradicts any axiom or previously deduced theorem. But how can we be sure that a particular set of axioms will never lead to a contradiction? The answer is that in general we cannot. The best we can do is show relative consistency; i.e., exhibit a model of the system by assigning meanings to the undefined terms in such a way that the axioms are judged to be valid. This will show that the axiom system is consistent if the model is consistent.

Beltrami, in 1868, was the first to exhibit a consistency model for hyperbolic geometry in Euclidean space, thus showing that hyperbolic geometry is consistent if Euclidean geometry is consistent. Before this, though no accepted contradictions had been found in the new geometry, there was always the possibility that one might be detected. Beltrami used a surface of constant negative curvature in three-dimensional Euclidean space called a *pseudosphere*. This surface is generated by revolving a tractrix about its asymptote. (A tractrix is a curve having the property that the part of the tangent between the point of tangency and a given straight line is of constant length. The given line is its asymptote.) By defining a "line" joining two points on the surface as the geodesic (curve of shortest length) between the points, Beltrami showed that the geometry of a limited region of the hyperbolic plane is that of a region on the pseudosphere. Figure 2.71

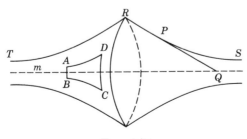

Fig. 2.71

shows tractrix TRS (tangent PQ constant) revolved about line m to give a pseudosphere on which is drawn a Saccheri quadrilateral $ABCD$. Other models of the hyperbolic plane will be discussed in more detail in later chapters.

2.8   Independence of Axioms

An axiom is said to be *independent* if it is not a logical consequence of the other axioms of the axiom system. A system of axioms is independent if each axiom of the system is independent. To show the independence of a given axiom of a set we produce a model in which all the other axioms of the set and the negation of the given one are satisfied. This must be done for each axiom of the set. Thus the discovery of non-Euclidean geometry established the independence of Euclid's parallel postulate.

Independence is not a necessary property for an axiom system. A mathematician prefers an axiom system not to say too much; i.e., it should not contain an axiom or part of one which can be proven on the basis of the other axioms. For pedagogical reasons, however, it is often desirable to include some provable statements in our axioms. Compare, for example, Hilbert's Axiom III–5 with SMSG Axiom 15.

2.9   Completeness and Categoricalness

Just as independence assures that an axiom system does not say too much, the property of completeness assures us that the system says enough. A set of axioms is said to be *complete* if it is impossible to add a new independent axiom which is consistent with the given set and which does not contain any new undefined terms. (The given set is assumed to be consistent.) Thus any statement formed in terms of the concepts of the system must be either provable or disprovable if the system is complete. Thus we see that Euclid's axiom system was incomplete because there were certain statements which were neither provable nor disprovable; e.g., "a line joining a point inside a circle to a point outside must intersect the circle." We see that Hilbert's axioms would be incomplete without the parallel postulate because it would then be possible to add a new independent axiom to the set; namely, either the Euclidean or the hyperbolic parallel postulate. However, we do not try to show completeness by failing to find new independent axioms, just as we did not try to prove consistency by developing theorem after theorem and failing to find one that contradicted an axiom or previously proven theorem. We use a property called categoricalness which can be shown to imply completeness.

A set of axioms is said to be *categorical* if it is possible to set up an *isomorphism* between any two models of the set; i.e., if there exists a one-to-one correspondence between the elements and relations of one model and those of the other such that whenever a given relation holds between two elements of one model, the corresponding relation holds between the corresponding two elements of the other.

It is not necessary that a set of axioms be categorical, nor is it even always desirable. For example, the axioms for a field are not categorical since they hold for the set of rational numbers and for the set of real numbers, two sets which are not isomorphic. Yet the development of the theory of arbitrary fields is fruitful in that it gives properties common to many different systems. A categorical set of axioms, on the other hand, yields essentially one mathematical system.

In definitions we usually insist upon both independence and completeness. For example, the definition of a parallelogram in the Euclidean plane as a quadrilateral with both pairs of opposite sides equal and parallel is not acceptable because these properties are not independent; nor is the definition of a square as a quadrilateral with four equal sides acceptable because it is not complete.

Exercises

1. Using the axiom system of Sec. 2.6, (a) prove that if aRb is true, then bRa is false. (b) Show that the set is consistent and independent but not categorical.

2. Test the independence of the parts of the following definition of a square: (a) it is a quadrilateral, (b) all of its sides are equal, and (c) all of its angles are equal.

3. Test the independence of the parts of the following definition of a regular pentagon: it is a convex polygon with (a) five sides, (b) all its sides are equal, and (c) all its angles are equal.

4. Test the independence of the parts of the following definition of a regular triangle: it is a polygon (a) with three sides, (b) all its sides are equal, and (c) all its angles are equal.

5. A binary relation R between elements $a, b, c, \cdots$ of a set S is an *equivalence relation* if, for all elements in S (a) aRa, (b) if aRb, then bRa, and (c) if aRb and bRc, then aRc. Show that these three conditions are independent.

2.10   A Finite Geometry*

We now illustrate the above concepts by examining in some detail an axiom system for a well-known finite geometry. A *finite geometry* is a geometry based on a system of axioms and undefined terms which limits the set of elements to a finite number.

Let S be a set of undefined elements $A, B, C, \cdots$ and let S have certain undefined subsets any one of which will be called an m-set. The relations

*Reprinted by permission of the publisher, from Oswald Veblen and John Wesley Young, *Projective Geometry*, Vol. I (Waltham, Massachusetts: Blaisdell Publishing Company, 1938), pp. 2–5.

"belonging to a set" and "containing an element" will be undefined. The following set of axioms is assumed:

1. If A and B are distinct elements of S there is at least one m-set containing A and B.
2. If A and B are distinct elements of S there is not more than one m-set containing A and B.
3. Any two m-sets have at least one element of S in common.
4. There exists at least one m-set.
5. Every m-set contains at least three elements of S.
6. All the elements of S do not belong to the same m-set.
7. No m-set contains more than three elements of S.

For *consistency* we exhibit the following symbolic diagram as a model:

$$A \quad B \quad C \quad D \quad E \quad F \quad G$$
$$B \quad C \quad D \quad E \quad F \quad G \quad A$$
$$D \quad E \quad F \quad G \quad A \quad B \quad C$$

The letters represent elements of S; the vertical columns represent m-sets.

The student should verify this model and the others that follow. A "geometric" model is shown in Fig. 2.10 1 where the elements are represented by points, and the m-sets by lines. In order to have all the axioms hold, we call BCE also a line. For *independence* we must exhibit seven models, one for each postulate. We list these below using the symbol (k') for the model in which all the axioms are valid except axiom k, where $k = 1,2,\cdots 7$.

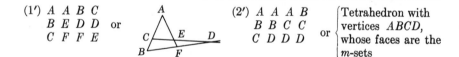

(1') $A \; A \; B \; C$
     $B \; E \; D \; D$ or
     $C \; F \; F \; E$

(2') $A \; A \; A \; B$
     $B \; B \; C \; C$ or $\begin{cases} \text{Tetrahedron with} \\ \text{vertices } ABCD, \\ \text{whose faces are the} \\ m\text{-sets} \end{cases}$
     $C \; D \; D \; D$

(3') $A \; A \; A \; A \; B \; B \; B \; C \; C \; C \; D \; G$
     $B \; D \; E \; F \; E \; D \; F \; D \; E \; F \; E \; H$
     $C \; G \; I \; H \; H \; I \; G \; H \; G \; I \; F \; I$

(4')   A single element. (The remaining postulates are fulfilled vacuously.)

(5') $A \; B \; C$
     $B \; C \; A$ or $\triangle ABC$

(6') A
     B or $\begin{cases} \text{A single line containing} \\ \text{three points.} \end{cases}$
     C

(7') **The real** projective plane, which we will take up in the next chapter.

We postpone the question of categoricalness until after we have proven some theorems. These must be proven by purely logical deduction without referring to any model. Any theorem thus proven will automatically be valid for any model of the axiom system.

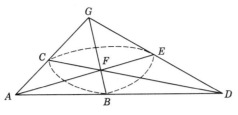

Fig. 2.10 1

We note first that Axioms 1 and 3 are *duals* of each other; i.e., by interchanging the undefined terms "element" and "*m*-set," and by interchanging the two undefined relations, Axiom 1 becomes Axiom 3 and vice versa. To establish complete duality we must prove the duals of the remaining axioms as theorems. These are the first five theorems below, proofs of which are left to the student. We note here that if the duals of all the axioms are valid then the duals of all theorems are also valid and hence need not be proven separately.

THEOREM 2.10 1 (DUAL OF AXIOM 2) *Two distinct m-sets have only one element in common.*

THEOREM 2.10 2 (DUAL OF AXIOM 4) *There exists at least one element in S.*

THEOREM 2.10 3 (DUAL OF AXIOM 5) *Every element belongs to at least three m-sets.*

THEOREM 2.10 4 (DUAL OF AXIOM 6) *No one element is contained in all the m-sets.*

THEOREM 2.10 5 (DUAL OF AXIOM 7) *No element belongs to more than three m-sets.*

THEOREM 2.10 6 *There exist exactly seven elements in S.*

Proof: Let A, B, C, D be the four elements guaranteed by Axioms 4, 5, 6, of which A, B, D belong to one *m*-set and C does not. (The lettering used is that of the abstract model.) Then by Axiom 1, A and C belong to another *m*-set, which, by Axiom 5, contains another element G. Similarly B and C belong to another *m*-set which contains a new element E; and B and G give a new *m*-set and a new element F. Other *m*-sets are obtained by using

Axioms 3 and 5. We now have seven elements. Assume that there is an eighth element H. Then the new m-set determined by A and H could not have an element in common with an existing m-set without violating Theorem 2.10 1.

THEOREM 2.10 7   (Dual of Theorem 2.10 6). *There exist exactly seven m-sets.*

These last two theorems enable us to see that any model for this finite geometry can be put into one-to-one correspondence with the symbolic consistency model so that the two models will be isomorphic. Thus we establish *categoricalness* for this system. That the model need not be mathematical is illustrated as follows: Rewrite the axioms replacing "element" by "student," and "m-set" by "committee," and consider the following problem: A group S of students has assembled in a room and has formed committees in accordance with the set of axioms as rewritten. How many students are there in the room and how many committees are formed?

Exercises

1. Verify the models for consistency and independence given in Sec. 2.10 and prove Theorems 2.10 1 – 2.10 5.

2. Show that the following set of axioms is consistent and independent, and show also that this finite geometry has the property of duality: *Axiom* 1: There exist exactly three distinct elements. *Axiom* 2: Two distinct elements belong to one and only one m-set. *Axiom* 3: Not all elements belong to the same m-set. *Axiom* 4: Two distinct m-sets have at least one element in common.

3. Show that the following axiom set is consistent and independent: *Axiom* 1: Two distinct elements belong to one and only one m-set. *Axiom* 2: There exists at least one m-set. *Axiom* 3: Each m-set contains exactly two elements. *Axiom* 4: Corresponding to each m-set there is exactly one m-set which has no element in common with it.

4. Given the following axiom set: *Axiom* 1: There exist exactly four distinct elements. *Axiom* 2: Two distinct elements belong to one and only one m-set. *Axiom* 3: Every m-set contains exactly two elements.

(a) Prove the following theorems:

THEOREM 1:   *There exist exactly 6 m-sets.*

DEFINITION: Two m-sets are parallel if they contain no common element.

THEOREM 2:   *Given an element A and an m-set not containing A, there exists one and only one m-set containing A and parallel to the given m-set.*

(b) Show that the axiom set is consistent and independent.

(c) Verify the following model for the axiom set: The 4 elements are the following number triples (x, y, z): $A(1, 0, 0)$, $B(0, 1, 0)$, $C(0, 0, 1)$, $D(1, 1, 1)$. The 6 m-sets are the following equations: $x = 0$, $y = 0$, $z = 0$, $x = y$, $y = z$, $z = x$. An element "belongs to" an m-set, or an m-set "contains" an element if and only if the number triple satisfies the equation.

In the following exercises test the validity of Hilbert's axioms of connection, order (use II–4' instead of II–4), and parallelism if the undefined terms are defined as stated:

5. Let "point" be an ordinary Euclidean point inside a given circle, let "line" be an open chord of the circle, and let point B be "between" A and C if A, B, C are on the same open chord and in the order (ABC).

6. Let "point" be an ordinary point on an open Euclidean hemisphere, let "line" be an open great semicircle on the hemisphere, and let point B be "between" A and C if A, B, C are on the same open semicircle and in the order (ABC).

7. Let "point" be any point on the surface of a Euclidean sphere except a given point P; let "line" be any circle on the sphere going through P (P is not to be considered as being a point on the line), and let point B be "between" A and C if the arc ABC does not contain P and if the order is (ABC).

8. Let "point" be an ordinary point in the Euclidean plane except a given point P; let "line" be any Euclidean circle or line through P (P is not to be considered as being on the line), and let "between" be defined as in Exercise 7 above.

9. Let "point" be an ordered pair of real numbers (x, y); let "line" be any equation of the form $ax + by + c = 0$, where a, b, c are real numbers, where a and b are not both zero and where $k(ax + by + c) = 0$ is the same line as $ax + by + c = 0$ for $k \neq 0$. Let point (x_3, y_3) be "between" points (x_1, y_1) and (x_2, y_2) if and only if there is a real number t, where $0 < t < 1$, such that $x_3 = (1 - t)x_1 + tx_2$, and $y_3 = (1 - t)y_1 + ty_2$.

10. Discuss the following statements:

"Mathematics may be defined as the subject in which we never know what we are talking about, nor whether what we are saying is true."

(Bertrand Russell)

"Mathematics is a game played according to certain simple rules with meaningless marks on paper."

(David Hilbert)

References

Adler, Chap. 2; Blumenthal, Chap. III; Eves, Chap. VIII; Eves and Newsom, Chap. VI; Kutuzov, Chap. XIII; Meserve, Chap. 1; Prenowitz and Jordan, Chap. 8; Stabler, Chaps. VII, VIII; Wilder, Chaps. I, II; Young (1), Chaps. II, IV, V.

CHAPTER 3

PLANE PROJECTIVE GEOMETRY

3.1 Introduction

The roots of projective geometry can be traced back to the ancient Greeks who knew some of the theorems as part of Euclidean geometry. Its formal development may be said to have been started in the 15th century by artists who were looking for a theory of perspective drawing; i.e., the laws of constructing the projections of three-dimensional objects on a two-dimensional plane. The theory was extended by Desargues (1593–1662), an engineer and architect who, in 1639, published a treatise on conic sections using the concept of projection. It was here that Desargues used the idea of adding one point "at infinity" to each line with the locus of these "ideal points" forming an "ideal line," added to the Euclidean plane, where parallel lines were to intersect (cf. Sec. 1.4). However, it was not until Monge (1746–1818), with his co-workers at the Ecole Polytechnique in Paris, developed his descriptive geometry—the analysis and representation of three-dimensional objects by means of their projections on different planes—that the study of projective geometry began to flourish.

Mathematicians classified geometric properties into two categories: *metric* properties, which are those concerned with measurements of distances, angles, and areas, and *descriptive* properties, which are those concerned with the positional relations of geometric figures to one another. For example, the length of a line segment and the congruence of two angles are metric properties, but the collinearity of three points and the concurrence of three lines are descriptive properties. In the case of plane figures, descriptive properties are preserved when a figure is projected from one plane onto another (provided we consider parallel lines as intersecting at an "ideal point"), while metric properties may not be preserved. Thus the property of a given curve being a circle is a metric property but that of its being a conic is a descriptive or projective property.

The beginning of the modern period of the development of projective geometry is usually placed at 1822 when Poncelet (1788–1867), a pupil of Monge, published his great treatise on the projective properties of figures, written while he was a prisoner in Russia. Throughout the 19th century, the subject was developed rapidly by Gergonne, Brianchon, Plucker, Steiner, Von Staudt and others.

For the most part, however, projective geometry was developed as an extension of Euclidean geometry; e.g., the parallel postulate was still used and a line was added to the Euclidean plane to contain the "ideal points" mentioned above. Two parallel lines had a unique common "ideal point"; while two intersecting lines had two different "ideal points" since they already had one point of intersection. The totality of "ideal points" formed an "ideal line." Thus it followed that two distinct points determine exactly one line *and* two distinct lines determine exactly one point. It was only at the end of the 19th century and the beginning of the 20th century, through the work of Felix Klein (1849–1925), Oswald Veblen (1880–1960), Hilbert, and others, that projective geometry was seen to be independent of the theory of parallels. Projective geometry was then developed as an abstract science based on its own set of axioms.

For an introduction to projective geometry as part of or as an extension of Euclidean geometry, see the references listed at the end of this section. We shall now develop some plane projective geometry as the study of theorems deduced from a set of axioms.

References

Adler, Chaps. 3 and 6; Courant and Robbins, Chap. IV; Eves, Chaps. II and VI; Fishback, Chap. 4; Graustein, Chap. II; Hilbert and Cohn-Vossen, Chap. III; Seidenberg, Chap. I; Young (2), Chaps. I and II.

3.2 Axioms of Incidence and the Principle of Duality

Consider a set of undefined elements called *points*, denoted by the letters $A, B, C, \cdots$, a second set of undefined elements called *lines*, denoted by the letters $a, b, c, \cdots$ and an undefined relation called *incidence*, applied to a point and a line. When a point and a line are *incident*, we say that the point *lies on* the line, or that the line *contains* the point, or that the line *goes through* the point. Points incident with the same line are said to be *collinear;* lines incident with the same point are said to be *concurrent.* (The student is again reminded that even though by using the vocabulary above we have an interpretation or model of our abstract science in mind and shall even draw figures from time to time, we must not draw inferences from the model which are not explicitly stated as axioms or deduced from them). The following axioms of incidence are assumed:

Axiom 1: There exist a point and a line that are not incident.

Axiom 2: Every line is incident with at least three points.

Axiom 3: Any two distinct points *A*, *B* are incident with one and only one line. This line is called the *join* of the two points and will be denoted by *AB*.

Axiom 4: Any two distinct lines *a*, *b* are incident with at least one point.

The student should have no trouble showing that these four axioms are consistent and independent, and that the following two theorems hold:

THEOREM 3.21   *Any two distinct lines a, b are incident with at most one point. The point is called the intersection of the two lines and will be denoted by a·b.*

THEOREM 3.22   *Every point is incident with at least three lines.*

DEFINITION 3.21   Any system of two sets of elements (which may be called points and lines) connected by a relation (which may be called incidence) for which the above axioms are verified, is called a *projective plane*. The associated geometry (the set of theorems deduced from these axioms) is called a *projective geometry*.

The seven point geometry of Sec. 2.10 is a *finite projective geometry*. There are of course other finite projective planes but every such plane must contain at least seven distinct points. See Exercises 8–11 at the end of this section for an answer to the question of how many points a finite projective plane may have.

A projective plane possesses a very important characteristic known as

DEFINITION 3.22   THE PRINCIPLE OF DUALITY: Any valid statement concerning the elements in a projective plane remains valid when we interchange the words *point* and *line* (and hence also *lie on* and *contain*, *join* and *intersection*, *collinear* and *concurrent*). The two statements are said to be *duals* of each other.

We note that Theorem 3.21 with Axiom 4 constitute the dual of Axiom 3, that Theorem 3.22 is the dual of Axiom 2 and that Axiom 1 is self-dual. Therefore, since the axioms imply their duals, then whenever we prove a new theorem based on these, its dual will be valid without further proof.

Exercises

1. Show that the four axioms of incidence are consistent and independent.
2. Prove Theorem 3.21.
3. Prove Theorem 3.22.

4. Show that in a projective plane there exist four points, no three of which are collinear.

5. Verify the following model of a projective plane: Let the "points" and "lines" be those of a Euclidean plane with the addition of one line, called the ideal line, where parallel lines are to intersect. Each line other than the ideal line contains one and only one ideal point. Let "incidence" have the conventional meaning (see Sec. 3.1).

6. Verify the following model of a projective plane: Let P be a given point in Euclidean three-dimensional space. Let "point" be a Euclidean line through P; let "line" be a Euclidean plane through P; and let "point A is incident with line a" mean that the Euclidean line A through point P lies on the Euclidean plane a through P.

7. Write the duals of the following and draw figures to illustrate the original and its dual: (a) Three non-collinear points and the three lines determined by them. (b) Four points, no three of which are collinear, and the six lines determined by them. (c) Three concurrent lines a, b, c through point O, and their points of intersection with a fourth line d not through O. (d) The line determined by points A and B intersecting the line determined by the points A and D in the point E.

8. Prove that if there are exactly n points on one line of a finite projective plane, then there are exactly n points on every line of the plane. State the dual of this theorem.

9. Prove that if there are exactly n points on one line of a finite projective plane, then there are exactly n lines through every point of the plane.

10. Prove that if there are exactly n points on a line of a finite projective plane, then the plane contains exactly $n^2 - n + 1$ points.

11. Show that a projective plane must contain at least seven points.

3.3   Desarguesian Projective Planes

We now begin to extend the set of axioms in order that we may eventually be able to obtain the geometry of the real projective plane.

DEFINITION 3.31   Three non-collinear points and the three lines determined by them form a *triangle*. The three points are called the *vertices* and the three lines the *sides* of the triangle.

DEFINITION 3.32   Two triangles are said to be *perspective from a point O* if there is a one-to-one correspondence between the vertices so that lines joining corresponding vertices all go through O. Dually, two triangles are said to be *perspective from a line o* if there is a one-to-one correspondence between the sides of the triangles such that the points of intersection of corresponding sides all lie on o.

Axiom 5: If two triangles are perspective from a point, then they are perspective from a line.

Axiom 5 is known in classical projective geometry as Desargues' Theorem and may be proven if other axioms are added to introduce points outside the plane [See Coxeter (1), p. 6]. That it cannot be deduced from the first four axioms was shown by exhibiting non-Desarguesian projective planes. One example may be found in Robinson, pp. 126–128.

To show that the principle of duality holds we now prove the dual of Axiom 5.

THEOREM 3.31   *If two triangles are perspective from a line then they are perspective from a point* (Fig. 3.31).

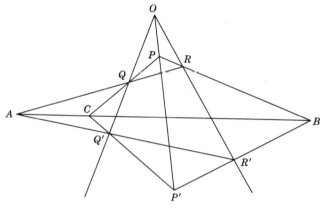

FIG. 3.31

ΔPQR and $\Delta P'Q'R'$ are given perspective from line ABC. From Axiom 4 we know that $Q'Q$ and $P'P$ meet in a point O. We must show that $R'R$ goes through O. For this we apply Axiom 5 to $\Delta AQQ'$ and $\Delta BPP'$ which are perspective from C and hence the intersections of corresponding sides (O, R', R) are collinear.

Exercises

1. Show that Axiom 5 is verified in the finite projective plane of Sec. 2.10.

2. Construct a 13-point finite projective plane and show that Axiom 5 is verified (Levy, p. 128).

3. Figure 3.31 is known as a *Desarguesian configuration*. It contains 10 distinct points. Show that any one of these 10 points can be taken as the center of perspectivity for two triangles forming a Desarguesian configuration with the *same* 10 points.

4. If the vertices of ΔPQR lie respectively on the sides of ΔABC so that AP, BQ, and CR are concurrent, and if $AB \cdot PQ = U$, $AC \cdot PR = V$, and $BC \cdot QR = W$, show that U, V, W are collinear.

*5. Justify the following instructions for the construction of a line joining a given point Q to the inaccessible point of intersection P of two given lines a and b: Let O (Fig. 3.32) be an arbitrary point and p_1, p_2, p_3 be three arbitrary lines

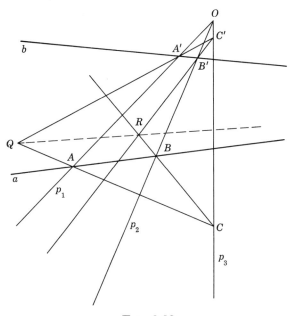

FIG. 3.32

through O. Let $a \cdot p_1 = A$, $b \cdot p_1 = A'$, $a \cdot p_2 = B$, $b \cdot p_2 = B'$, $AQ \cdot p_3 = C$, $A'Q \cdot p_3 = C'$ and $BC \cdot B'C' = R$. Then the required line is QR.

3.4   Harmonic Sets

DEFINITION 3.41   Four points P, Q, R, S, of which no three are collinear, are the vertices of a *complete quadrangle*† of which the six sides are QR, PS, RP, QS, PQ, RS. The three points A, B, C, which are the intersections of opposite sides, are called the *diagonal points* of the quadrangle [Fig. 3.41(a) and (b)]. Dually, four lines p, q, r, s, of which no three are concurrent, are the sides of a *complete quadrilateral* whose six vertices are $ABCDEF$ where $A = p \cdot r$, $B = p \cdot s$, $C = p \cdot q$, $D = q \cdot s$, $E = q \cdot r$, $F = r \cdot s$. The three lines a, b, c, which are the joins of opposite vertices, are called the *diagonal lines* of the quadrilateral (Fig. 3.42).

*Reprinted by permission of the publishers from Argunov and Skornyakov, *Configuration Theorems* (D. C. Heath and Co., 1963).
†The student should prove that such a figure exists (Sec. 3.2, Ex. 4).

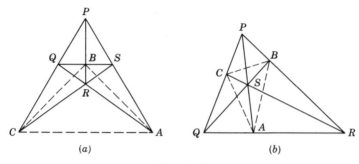

FIG. 3.41

Note the resemblance of Fig. 3.41 (b) to the geometric model of the finite geometry of Sec. 2.10 where the diagonal points were on a line. We now eliminate this possibility by adding another axiom.

Axiom 6: The diagonal points of a complete quadrangle are not collinear. They are vertices of a triangle called the *diagonal triangle* of the quadrangle.

To show that the principle of duality holds we must prove the dual of Axiom 6.

THEOREM 3.41   *The diagonal lines of a complete quadrilateral are not concurrent.*

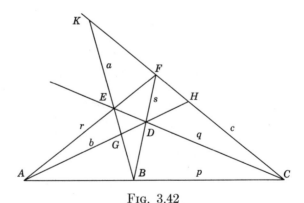

FIG. 3.42

Using the notation of the definition, let $a \cdot b = G$, $a \cdot c = K$, $b \cdot c = H$ (Fig. 3.42). We must show that G, H, K are not all the same point. Assume that diagonal line c does go through G. Then consider quadrangle $AEDB$ whose diagonal points are G, C, F. Since line c goes through C and F, this would make G, C, F collinear and contradict Axiom 6.

DEFINITION 3.42 Four collinear points A, B, C, D are said to form a *harmonic set* if there is a quadrangle of which two opposite sides pass through A, two other opposite sides pass through B, while the two remaining sides pass through C and D, respectively. We say that C and D are *harmonic conjugates* of each other with respect to A and B, and write this as $H(A, B, C, D)$ or $H(B, A, C, D)$ or $H(A, B, D, C)$ or $H(B, A, D,C)$.

If we are given three collinear points A, B, C, we may construct point D such that $H(A, B, C, D)$ as follows (Fig. 3.43): Draw any other two lines

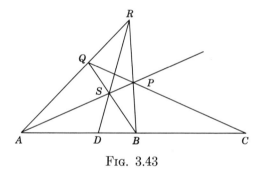

FIG. 3.43

through A. Take any point P ($\neq A$) on one of them. Let CP intersect the other line in Q, and let BP intersect this same line in R. Let $BQ \cdot AP = S$. Then the required point $D = RS \cdot AB$. Since this construction involves the arbitrary choice of two lines and a point, will any such choice always yield the same point D? The following theorem proves it will.

THEOREM 3.42 *If A, B, C are three collinear points, then the harmonic conjugate of C with respect to A and B is unique.*

Let $PQRS$ and $P'Q'R'S'$ be two quadrangles used as in the above construction to determine point D (Fig. 3.44). We must show that RS and $R'S'$ intersect line AB at the same point D. Since $\triangle PQR$ and $\triangle P'Q'R'$ are perspective from line ABC they are also perspective from some point O (not shown); i.e., RR', PP', and QQ' go through O. Doing the same for $\triangle PQS$ and $\triangle P'Q'S'$ we find that SS' also goes through O. Hence $\triangle RSP$ and $\triangle R'S'P'$ are perspective from O and therefore must be perspective from a line.

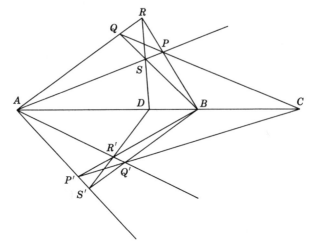

FIG. 3.44

But $RP \cdot R'P' = B$, and $SP \cdot S'P' = A$. Therefore RS and $R'S'$ must intersect in a point D on AB.

THEOREM 3.43 $H(A, B, C, D)$ *implies* $H(C, D, A, B)$ (Fig. 3.45).

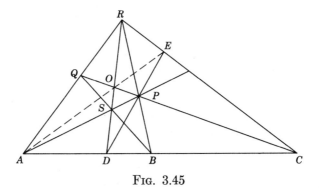

FIG. 3.45

Let $PQRS$ be a quadrangle giving $H(A, B, C, D)$. Let $DP \cdot RC = E$, and $PQ \cdot RS = O$. Then $\triangle QOS$ and $\triangle REP$ are perspective from line CDB and must therefore be perspective from a point. But $QR \cdot SP = A$. Therefore OE goes through A, and quadrangle $OPER$ gives $H(C, D, A, B)$. The pairs of points A, B and C, D are called *pairs of the harmonic set*.

The student should now formulate the definition of a harmonic set of lines and duals of the last two theorems.

Exercises

1. Show that if ABC (Fig. 3.41) is the diagonal triangle of quadrangle $PQRS$ and if $X = BC \cdot QR$, $Y = CA \cdot RP$, $Z = AB \cdot PQ$, then X, Y, Z are collinear.

2. State the dual of Exercise 1 and draw diagrams to illustrate both.

3. Given the diagonal triangle and one vertex of a quadrangle, construct the complete quadrangle. Is it unique?

4. Define a harmonic set of lines, and construct a line d such that $H(a, b, c, d)$ when three concurrent lines a, b, c are given.

5. State and illustrate the duals of Theorems 3.42 and 3.43.

6. Show that Axiom 6 assures us that the four points of a harmonic set are distinct and thus that there are at least four points on every line.

7. What model shows the independence of Axiom 6?

8. In the model of Ex. 5 of Sec. 3.2, construct the harmonic conjugate of C with respect to A and B if (a) C is the ideal point on line AB, (b) C is the midpoint of segment AB.

3.5   Perspectivities and Projectivities

DEFINITION 3.51   On a plane, the set of all lines through a point P is called a *pencil of lines;* the set of all points on a line p is called a *pencil of points.*

DEFINITION 3.52   A one-to-one correspondence between points X on line p and points X' on line p' such that line XX' goes through a fixed point O, is called a *perspectivity with center O*, and is written $X \overset{O}{\underset{\wedge}{=}} X'$ [(Fig. 3.51(a)]. Dually, a one-to-one correspondence between lines x through

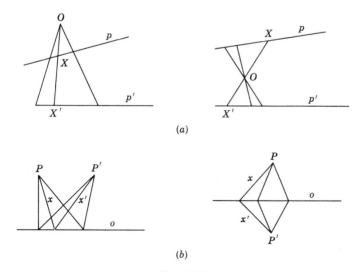

(a)

(b)

FIG. 3.51

point P and lines x' through P' such that points $x \cdot x'$ lie on a fixed line o, is called a *perspectivity with axis* o, and is written $x \overset{o}{\underset{\wedge}{=}} x'$ [Fig. 3.51(b)].

Also, a correspondence between a pencil of lines through P and a pencil of points on p (P not on p) is a perspectivity if every line of the pencil of lines goes through the corresponding point of the pencil of points.

Thus a perspectivity between two pencils of elements may be a perspectivity between two pencils of points, between two pencils of lines, or between a pencil of points and a pencil of lines. In the last case we say that either pencil is a *section* of the other.

DEFINITION 3.53   A correspondence between elements of two pencils is called a *projectivity* if it is made up of a finite sequence of perspectivities (symbol: $X \overline{\wedge} X'$). We shall also say that two such pencils are *projectively related*. Sections of two projectively related pencils are therefore also projectively related.

Note that a projectivity may be a correspondence between the elements of two pencils of points *on the same line* (or two pencils of lines through the same point). For example, in Fig. 3.52 $ABC \overset{P}{\underset{\wedge}{=}} A'B'C' \overset{Q}{\underset{\wedge}{=}} DEF$, and therefore $ABC \overline{\wedge} DEF$.

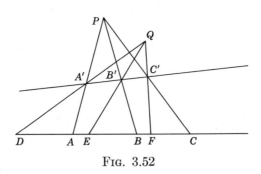

Fig. 3.52

THEOREM 3.51   *If four elements of a pencil form a harmonic set, then the four elements corresponding to them under a perspectivity also form a harmonic set; i.e., the harmonic relation is invariant under a perspectivity.*

We shall start with four points A, B, C, D such that $H(A, B, C, D)$. Choose point O not on line AB and join it to A, B, C, D by lines a, b, c, d, respectively (Fig. 3.53). We shall prove that $H(a, b, c, d)$. Draw a line through

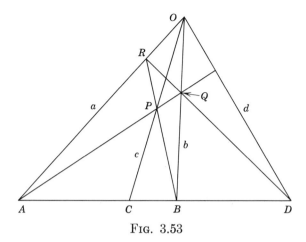

FIG. 3.53

A meeting OC in P and OB in Q. Let $BP \cdot OA = R$. Then RQ goes through D. (Why?) But AD, AQ, RD, RB form a quadrilateral which has two opposite vertices (A, R) on a, two other opposite vertices (B, Q) on b, one vertex (P) on c, and one vertex (D) on d. Hence $H(a, b, c, d)$. The converse of the above follows by duality and from these the theorem is obtained.

THEOREM 3.52   *The harmonic relation is invariant under a projectivity.*

This follows from Definition 3.53 and Theorem 3.51.

THEOREM 3.53   *A projectivity may be set up whenever three distinct elements of one pencil and the corresponding three elements of another are given.*

We prove this for two pencils of points and leave it to the student to prove for the other cases.

Let A, B, C be three distinct points on p (Fig. 3.54), and A', B', C' be the corresponding points on p'. If A and A' coincide then a single perspectivity is sufficient; i.e., the one having $BB' \cdot CC'$ as center. If $A \neq A'$, let P be a third point on line AA' and let p_1 be a line through A' meeting PB at B_1 and PC at C_1. Let $B_1B' \cdot C_1C' = Q$. Then $ABC \overset{P}{\underset{\wedge}{=}} A'B_1C_1 \overset{Q}{\underset{\wedge}{=}} A'B'C'$.

Therefore $ABC \overline{\wedge} A'B'C'$. The student may now show how to find X' on p' corresponding to any point X on p under this projectivity. If p and p' are the same line we may use an arbitrary perspectivity $ABC \overline{\wedge} A''B''C''$ to obtain three points on another line p'' and then proceed as above to get $A''B''C'' \overline{\wedge} A'B'C'$.

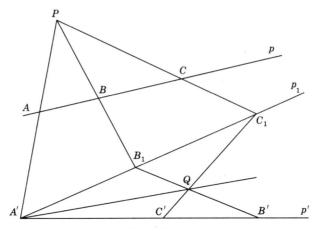

FIG. 3.54

Since the construction of the projectivity involves drawing arbitrary lines, we are again faced with the question of the uniqueness of the projectivity. Given *any* fourth point D on p, will it correspond to the *same* point D' on p' under two different constuctions of the projectivity under which $ABC \overline{\wedge} A'B'C'$? The affirmative answer to this question is known as the *Fundamental Theorem of Projective Geometry* and is sometimes taken as an axiom at this point. We shall postpone the question and later (Sec. 3.8) outline the proof for the real projective plane.

THEOREM 3.54 If $H(A, B, C, D)$ and $H(A', B', C', D')$, *then* $ABCD \overline{\wedge}$ $A'B'C'D'$.

This is an immediate consequence of Theorems 3.53, 3.52, and 3.42.

Exercises

1. In the projectivity given in Fig. 3.54, show how to find the point X' on p' corresponding to any point X on p.

2. Carry out the construction of Theorem 3.53 for a projectivity between two pencils of lines, and for a projectivity between a pencil of points and a pencil of lines.

3. Let $a_1, a_2, \cdots$ and $b_1, b_2, \cdots$ be two pencils of lines through the points A and B, respectively, such that $a_i \overline{\wedge} b_i$. Let p be a line not containing A or B and let $a_i \cdot p = P_i$ and $b_i \cdot p = Q_i$. Show that $P_i \overline{\wedge} Q_i$.

4. Let a, b, c be three concurrent lines and P, Q two points not on any of them. Let $A_1, A_2, \cdots$ and $B_1, B_2, \cdots$ be pencils of points on a and b, respectively, such that $A_i P \cdot B_i Q = C_i$ where C_i is on line c. Show that $A_i \overline{\wedge} B_i$.

5. Given four distinct collinear points A, B, C, D, construct the following projectivities: (a) $ABC \overline{\wedge} ABD$; (b) $ABC \overline{\wedge} ACD$; (c) $ABC \overline{\wedge} BAD$; (d) $ABC \overline{\wedge} ACB$ and find D' corresponding to D.

6. In the seven-point plane of Fig. 2.10, show that $ABD \barwedge BAD \barwedge DBA$.

7. In the model of Ex. 5 of Sec. 3.2, construct the projectivity $ABC \barwedge A'B'C'$ where A and B are two distinct points on a Euclidean line m whose ideal point is C, and A' and B' are two distinct points on a Euclidean line m' ($\neq m$) whose ideal point is C'.

8. Write out the proof of Theorem 3.54.

3.6 Axioms of Order

Before introducing a second undefined relation and new axioms to assure us an infinite number of points on every line, we present an intuitive introduction to show why the Euclidean concept of order on a line will not do for a projective line, and to suggest the approach to be taken.

Since *any* three distinct collinear points correspond under a projectivity to any three distinct collinear points (Th. 3.53), a relation involving three points cannot be invariant and hence can have no meaning in projective geometry. "Betweenness" is such a relation. This is illustrated in Fig. 3.61 where $ABC \overset{O}{\barwedge} A'B'C'$ and B is "between" A and C, but B' is not "between" A' and C'. An order relation on a projective line must therefore involve at least four points. Furthermore, the principle of duality in the

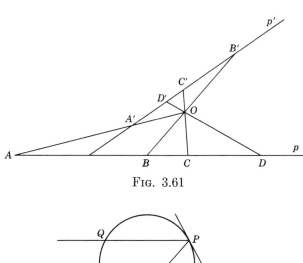

FIG. 3.61

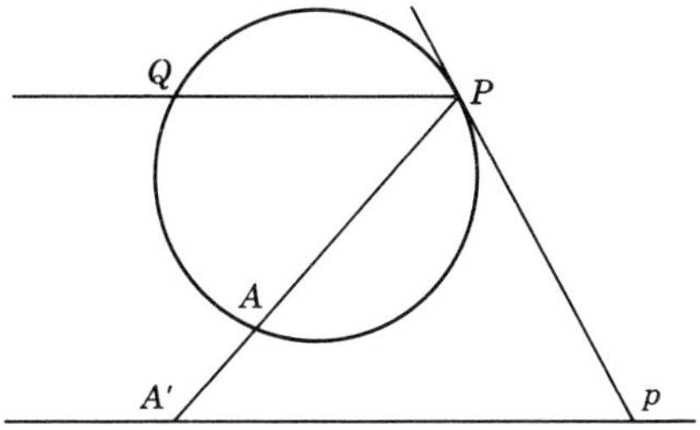

FIG. 3.62

projective plane shows us that a line, considered as a pencil of points, has properties of a pencil of lines, where order is cyclic. The projective line will be seen to have the order properties of a closed curve. In fact, in the model of Ex. 5 of Sec. 3.2, a one-to-one correspondence can be set up between the points on a Euclidean circle and the points on a projective line. This is shown in Fig. 3.62 where P is an arbitrary point on the circle. Any point A on the circle corresponds to point A' on the line p such that $A' = AP \cdot p$. P itself corresponds to the point of intersection of p with the tangent at P. The point Q such that $PQ \parallel p$ corresponds to the ideal point on p. This suggests using a circle to illustrate the order properties of a projective line (Fig. 3.63).

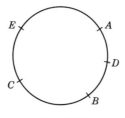

Fig. 3.63

We now introduce a second undefined relation called *separation*, applied to two pairs of points or to two pairs of lines. If the pairs of points A, B and C, D (or lines a, b and c, d) satisfy the relation, we say that the two pairs *separate each other*, and denote this by $AB//CD$ (*or* ab//cd). The following axioms are assumed:

Axiom 7: If $AB//CD$ then A, B, C, D are distinct and collinear and $BA//CD$, $AB//DC$, $BA//DC$, $CD//AB$, $CD//BA$, $DC//AB$, $DC//BA$.

Axiom 8: For any four distinct, collinear points A, B, C, D, at least two pairs must separate each other; i.e., at least one of the following holds: $AB//CD$, $AC//BD$, or $AD//BC$.

Axiom 9: If $AB//CD$ and $AC//BE$, then $AB//DE$.

Axiom 10: The separation relation is invariant under a perspectivity.

Axiom 7 says in effect that if two pairs of points separate each other, neither the order of points in each pair nor the order of the pairs affect the relation.

Axiom 10, which is self-dual, means that if four concurrent lines a, b, c, d

intersect a fifth line in four points A, B, C, D, then $AB//CD$ if and only if $ab//cd$. This then establishes the duals of Axioms 7, 8, and 9.

We notice that in the construction of a harmonic set (Sec. 3.4) the pairs of the set separate each other. We will now prove this, but we shall need a preliminary theorem first.

THEOREM 3.61 *For any four distinct, collinear points A, B, C, D, not more than one of the following holds:* $AB//CD$, $AC//BD$, $AD//BC$.

Axiom 8 states that at least one of these relations holds, say $AB//CD$. If $AC//BD$ also held, then by Axiom 9 we would have $AB//DD$ which contradicts Axiom 7. A similar thing happens if we assume that $AB//CD$ and $AD//BC$.

THEOREM 3.62 *The pairs of a harmonic set of points separate each other; i.e., if $H(A, B, C, D)$ then $AB//CD$.*

By Theorem 3.53 there exists a projectivity such that $ABC \barwedge ABD$ (cf. Ex. 5 of Sec. 3.5). Under this projectivity D corresponds to some point D'; i.e., $ABCD \barwedge ABDD'$. But if $H(A, B, C, D)$ then $H(A, B, D, C)$ and by Theorems 3.52 and 3.42 $D' = C$. Hence $ABCD \barwedge ABDC$. Now one of the three separation relations of Axiom 8 must hold. If $AC//BD$ then by Axiom 10, $AD//BC$ which contradicts Theorem 3.61. If $AD//BC$, we again arrive at a contradiction. Therefore $AB//CD$. By duality, the pairs of a harmonic set of lines separate each other.

DEFINITION 3.61 If A, B, C are three distinct points on a line, the *line segment* AB/C (read "AB without C") is the set of points X for which $AB//CX$. A and B are called the *endpoints* of the segment. Dually, if a, b, c are three distinct lines through a point, the *angular region* ab/c is the set of lines for which $ab//cx$.

It can be shown that if $AB//CD$ then A and B divide the line AB into just two segments: AB/C and AB/D [Coxeter (1), Chap. 3. See Theorem 5.38 for an analytic proof].

We have seen that a projective line has order properties of a Euclidean circle rather than those of a Euclidean line. It lacks, however, an important separation property that these two figures have. A Euclidean line (or circle) separates the remaining points of the plane into two sets such that if two points are in different sets, the line segment joining them intersects the line (or circle). The following theorem will show that two points in a projective plane are always on the *same* "side" of a given line.

THEOREM 3.63   *If p is any line in the projective plane, and A and B are any two points not on p, then there always exists a segment with endpoints A, B which does not intersect p.*

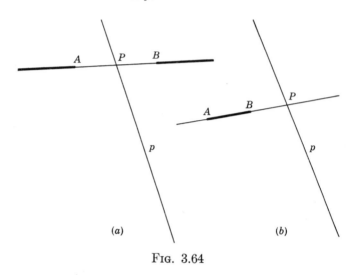

FIG. 3.64

Let $P = AB \cdot p$, where AB is the *line* determined by A and B. Then segment AB/P does not contain P and therefore does not intersect p. [See Fig. 3.64 (a) and (b) where segment AB/P is the heavy portion of the line.]

3.7   Net of Rationality and an Axiom of Continuity

We are now ready to set up a coordinate system for points on a projective line. Let us recall that for the real Euclidean line we chose two arbitrary reference points on the line to which we assigned the numbers 0 and 1, and used a distance concept and a continuity postulate to establish a one-to-one correspondence between the set of real numbers and the points on the line. For the projective line we do not have a distance concept. However, with the help of the projective postulates, the concept of a harmonic set of points, and a continuity postulate, we will show how a one-to-one correspondence can be set up between the set of real numbers and all but one of the points on the real projective line.

We start by choosing three arbitrary points as reference points on the projective line p. To two of them we assign the real numbers 0 and 1; to the third we assign the symbol ∞.* We call these points respectively the *zero point*, the *unit point*, and the *ideal point* of the line. In what follows we will sometimes use a number to designate a point. Thus the "point n"

*Care must be taken not to consider ∞ as anything but a symbol. In what follows, we shall give this symbol properties by definition as we need them.

will mean the point to which the number n has been assigned, or the point whose *coordinate* is n.

We proceed as follows (Fig. 3.71): Let q and r be two distinct lines through ∞ other than p. Let A be a point on r ($\neq \infty$). Join A to point 1

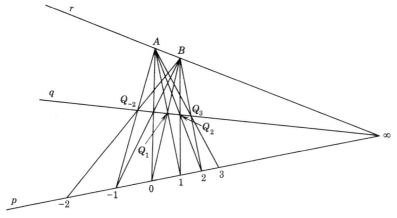

FIG. 3.71

and let Q_1 be the intersection of this line with q. Join Q_1 to point 0 and let B be the intersection of this line with r. Join B to point 1 and let Q_2 be the intersection of this line with q. Then the point 2 is the point $p \cdot AQ_2$. Note that $H(\infty, 1, 0, 2)$ from quadrangle ABQ_1Q_2, so that, by Theroem 3.42, the point 2 is unique; i.e., it is independent of the method of construction once the reference points are chosen. Now join B to 2 and let Q_3 be the point of intersection of this line with q. Then point 3 is the point $p \cdot AQ_3$. Note that $H(\infty, 2, 1, 3)$ from quadrangle ABQ_2Q_3. In this way we obtain points corresponding to the set of positive integers, where the point n ($n \geq 2$) is the point such that $H(\infty, n-1, n-2, n)$.

For the negative integers, join A to 0 and let Q_{-1} be the point of intersection of this line with q. Then point -1 is the point $p \cdot BQ_{-1}$. Note that $H(\infty, 0, -1, 1)$, which can be obtained from the above $H(\infty, n-1, n-2, n)$ by letting $n = 1$. Join A to -1 and let Q_{-2} be the point of intersection of this line with q. Then point -2 is the point $p \cdot BQ_{-2}$. We have $H(\infty, -1, -2, 0)$, which can be obtained from $H(\infty, n-1, n-2, n)$ by letting $n = 0$, etc. The order axioms assure us that these points on p are all distinct. (See Meserve, p. 81 for proof by mathematical induction.) Thus the order axioms assure us of an infinite number of points on a projective line.

Note that the points 0 and ∞ divide the line p into two segments, one of which contains all the points corresponding to the positive integers and the other contains the points corresponding to the negative integers. Furthermore, if an integer c is between* two integers a and b then the corresponding points are such that c is in segment ab/∞; i.e., $ab//c\infty$.

To obtain points with rational coordinates c/d where c and d are integers, we first let $1/d$ be the point such that $H(1, -1, d, 1/d)$ and then proceed as before using the three points 0, $1/d$, ∞ as the three starting points in place of 0, 1, ∞. We thus obtain c/d as the point such that

$$H\left(\infty, \frac{c-1}{d}, \frac{c-2}{d}, \frac{c}{d}\right).$$

The set of points thus obtained on p, the set corresponding to the set of rational numbers, is called a *net of rationality* determined by the points 0, 1, ∞. It is of interest to note here that even without the axioms of order we can carry out the construction for a net of rationality. But if the number of points on a line is finite the sequence will repeat itself.

To complete the real projective line by assuring the existence of a point on the line corresponding to a given irrational number, we shall need a continuity axiom. We can use the property that a given irrational number m can be expressed as a limit of a sequence of rational numbers, and then assume the sequence of points corresponding to these rational numbers has a limit point m on the line. As an alternative, we can adapt Dedekind's postulate of continuity (end of Appendix 2) to a projective line by defining "betweenness" as follows:

If A, B, C are three distinct points on a projective line, other than the point ∞, then C is between A and B if and only if C is in the segment AB/∞; i.e., $AB//C\infty$.

Both these approaches are to be understood in the following simple statement:

Axiom 11: The correspondence between the set of rational numbers and the net of rationality determined by three distinct points 0, 1, ∞ on a projective line can be extended to an isomorphism between the set of real numbers and all but the point ∞ on the line.

The dual of a net of rationality determined by three points on a line is a net of rationality determined by three lines through a point. The dual of Axiom 11 follows from the correspondence that can be set up between the lines of the pencil and the points of intersection of these lines with any line not in the pencil.

Between is being used here in terms of the order properties of the real numbers; i.e., c is between a and b if $a < c < b$ or if $b < c < a$.

This completes the set of axioms for the real projective plane. Unless otherwise stated, a line hereafter will refer to a real projective line.

Exercises

1. Given three points 0, 1, ∞ on a line, carry out the construction for the points 1/2, 1/3, 2/3, $-1/3$.

2. Use the method of this section to carry out the construction for the points 2, 3, -1, -2, 1/3, 2/3, $-1/3$ in the model of Ex. 5 of Sec. 3.2.

3. Verify the following model of a real projective plane: Let "point" be an ordinary point on a closed Euclidean hemisphere with opposite points on the boundary identified as a single point; let "line" be half a great circle on the hemisphere; let "separation" be the obvious relation of four points on a circle. (Note that this is precisely the model we get if we project the plane of Ex. 5 of Sec. 3.2 onto the lower hemisphere of a Euclidean sphere tangent to the plane, using the center of the sphere as the center of projection. This projection is called a *gnomonic* projection.)

3.8   The Fundamental Theorem of Projective Geometry and Pappus' Theorem

In this section we return to the question of the uniqueness of the projectivity set up when three pairs of corresponding elements are given (Theorem 3.53) and to some of its consequences. We start with a preliminary key theorem and an outline of its proof.

THEOREM 3.81   *If a projectivity between the points of a given line leaves three distinct points of the line fixed, it leaves every point of the line fixed.*

By the uniqueness of the fourth point of a harmonic set (Theorem 3.42) and by the invariance of the harmonic relation under projectivity (Theorem 3.52), if three points of a line are fixed then every point of the net of rationality determined by these three points is fixed. Then, by Axiom 11, all real points of the line are fixed. Such a projectivity is called the *identity* projectivity.

THEOREM 3.82   THE FUNDAMENTAL THEOREM OF PROJECTIVE GEOMETRY: *A projectivity between two pencils is completely determined by three distinct pairs of corresponding elements; i.e. (for pencils of points), if $ABCD \overline{\wedge} A'B'C'D'$ and if $ABCD \overline{\wedge} A'B'C'D''$, then $D' = D''$.*

From the definition of a projectivity we have $A'B'C'D' \overline{\wedge} ABCD \overline{\wedge} A'B'C'D''$ and hence $A'B'C'D' \overline{\wedge} A'B'C'D''$. Therefore, by Theorem 3.81, $D' = D''$. By duality we have the theorem for pencils of lines.

We now consider some basic consequences of this theorem.

THEOREM 3.83   *If in a projectivity between the points of two distinct lines, the point of intersection of the two lines corresponds to itself, then the projectivity is a perspectivity.*

Let the point of intersection $A = A'$ and let the projectivity be determined by $ABC \barwedge A'B'C'$. Then the perspectivity whose center is $BB' \cdot CC'$ satisfies the condition determining the projectivity.

For our next basic theorem we shall need some definitions.

DEFINITION 3.81   A *hexagon* is a figure formed by six distinct points, called *vertices*, which may be numbered $P_1 \cdots P_6$ and by six lines called the *sides*, joining the points P_1P_2, P_2P_3, P_3P_4, P_4P_5, P_5P_6, P_6P_1. (Figure 3.81 shows two illustrations of a hexagon.) The vertices P_1 and P_4, P_2

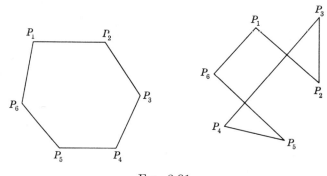

FIG. 3.81

and P_5, P_3 and P_6 are said to be pairs of *opposite vertices*, and the lines P_1P_2 and P_4P_5, P_2P_3 and P_5P_6, P_3P_4 and P_6P_1 are pairs of *opposite sides*. The three points of intersection of the three pairs of opposite sides are called the *diagonal points* of the hexagon.

THEOREM 3.84 (*Pappus' Theorem,* end of 3rd century A.D.)   *If alternate vertices of a hexagon lie on two lines, then the diagonal points are collinear.*

We are given hexagon $P_1P_2P_3P_4P_5P_6$ (Fig. 3.82), with P_1, P_3, P_5 on one line and P_2, P_4, P_6 on the second line. The diagonal points are A, B, C, which are to be proven collinear. Let $P_1P_6 \cdot P_4P_5 = D$ and $P_5P_6 \cdot P_3P_4 = E$. Now $P_4ADP_5 \overset{P_1}{\barwedge} P_4P_2P_6O \overset{P_3}{\barwedge} ECP_6P_5$. Hence $P_4ADP_5 \barwedge ECP_6P_5$ so that P_5 corresponds to itself. Therefore, by Theorem 3.83, the projectivity is a perspectivity. Hence P_4E, AC, DP_6 must be concurrent. But $P_4E \cdot DP_6$ is the point B, and thus AC goes through B.

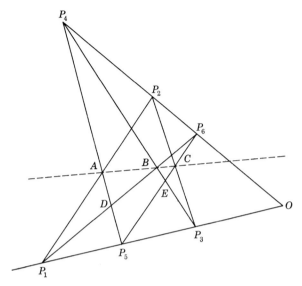

FIG. 3.82

The student should write out and draw figures for the duals of the above definitions and theorems.

In some developments of projective geometry, Pappus' Theorem is used as an axiom instead of Desargues' Theorem. Then Desargues' Theorem can be deduced [Coxeter (1), p. 41]. For an excellent account of the relations among the basic theorems of projective geometry, the student is referred to Seidenberg, Chap. IV.

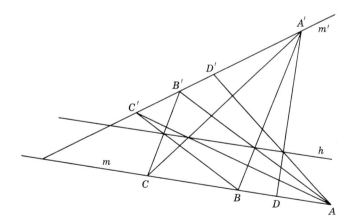

FIG. 3.83

Pappus' Theorem gives a convenient method of constructing a given projectivity between two pencils of points on two distinct lines. Let the given projectivity be determined by the three distinct points A, B, C on line m and the three distinct points A', B', C' on m' so that $ABC \overline{\wedge} A'B'C'$ (Fig. 3.83). Consider hexagon $AB'CA'BC'$. Its diagonal points are collinear giving line h, called the *axis of homology*. We shall show that if D is any point on m, and D' is the point on m' such that $ABCD \overline{\wedge} A'B'C'D'$, then D' is the point of intersection of m' with the line joining A to $h \cdot A'D$. The projectivity given establishes a projectivity between the two pencils of lines AA', AB', AC', AD' and $A'A$, $A'B$, $A'C$, $A'D$, in which line AA' is self-corresponding. Therefore, by the dual of Theorem 3.83, this is a perspectivity whose axis is h. The student should give the dual of this construction.

<h2>Exercises</h2>

1. Write and illustrate the dual of Theorem 3.83.

2. Write and illustrate the duals of Definition 3.81 and Theorem 3.84.

3. Show that Pappus' Theorem holds in the seven-point projective plane (Sec. 2.10).

4. Show how the dual of Pappus' Theorem can be used to give a construction for a projectivity between two pencils of lines through two distinct points.

5. Given three distinct lines p_1, p_2, p_3 concurrent at point P, and two distinct points Q and R not on any of the lines. Let $A_1B_1C_1$, $A_2B_2C_2$, and $A_3B_3C_3$ be triples of distinct points on p_1, p_2, p_3, respectively, such that none of these is P and such that $A_1B_1C_1 \overset{Q}{\overline{\wedge}} A_2B_2C_2 \overset{R}{\overline{\wedge}} A_3B_3C_3$. Prove that the projectivity $A_1B_1C_1 \overline{\wedge} A_3B_3C_3$ is a perspectivity and that its center is on line QR.

*6. Given point Q and an inaccessible point $P = a \cdot b$ (Fig. 3.84). Prove that the following construction gives line PQ: Let A_1 and A_2 be two arbitrary points on a,

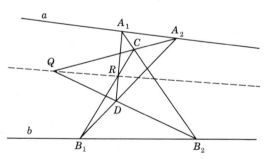

FIG. 3.84

*Reprinted by permission of the publishers from Argunov and Skornyakov, *Configuration Theorems* (D.C. Heath and Co., 1963).

and B_1 and B_2 be two arbitrary points on b. Let $C = A_1B_2 \cdot QA_2$, $D = A_2B_1 \cdot QB_2$, and $R = A_1D \cdot B_1C$. Then QR goes through P.

  7. In Fig. 3.82 show that $P_1P_5P_3O \mathbin{\overline{\wedge}} P_4P_2P_6R$, where $R = P_4O \cdot AB$.

  8. In Fig. 3.83 let $P = m \cdot m'$ and find the point corresponding to P if (a) P is considered as a point on m; (b) P is a point on m'.

3.9   Conics in the Projective Plane

We shall now take up a brief consideration of conics in the projective plane, a topic to which we shall return later.

DEFINITION 3.91 (Steiner, 1832)   The set of all points of intersection of pairs of corresponding lines of two projective, non-perspective pencils of lines through distinct points, is called a *point conic*. The dual definition gives a *line conic*.

If distinct lines a, b, c of a pencil through point P and distinct lines a', b', c' of a pencil through point P' ($P \neq P'$) are given, and if $A = a \cdot a'$, $B = b \cdot b'$, $C = c \cdot c'$ are not collinear, a non-perspective projectivity between the two pencils is determined and points A, B, C are on the conic thus generated (Fig. 3.91). Now to the line PP' considered as a line of the pen-

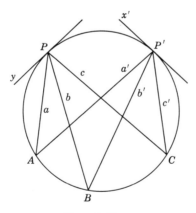

FIG. 3.91

cil through P, there corresponds a line x' of the pencil through P'. But $x' \cdot PP' = P'$, and hence P' is on the conic. Furthermore, x' does not intersect the conic in any point other than P'. A line intersecting a conic in only one point is called a *tangent* to the conic. Similarly, P is on the conic and the line y of the pencil through P, corresponding to PP' considered as a line of the pencil through P', is a tangent to the conic.

  Thus, if five points P, P', A, B, C, no three of which are collinear, are given, a conic is generated by the projectivity between the two pencils of lines through P and P' in which lines PA, PB, PC correspond to $P'A$, $P'B$, $P'C$, respectively. Now the question of uniqueness comes up again. If we used *any* two of the five points for the pencils of lines, would we get the *same* conic? We shall show that we do. We start with a preliminary theorem.

THEOREM 3.91   *If A, B, C, D are four points on a point conic generated by projective pencils through P and P' then the diagonal points of hexagon $PBP'ACD$ are collinear; and conversely, if the diagonal points are collinear for hexagon $PBP'ACD$ where no three vertices are collinear, then A, B, C, D are on the conic determined by the pencils through P and P' (Fig. 3.92).*

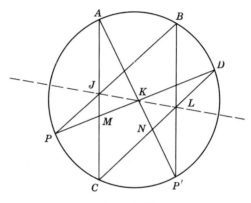

FIG. 3.92

Let $PB \cdot AC = J, BP' \cdot CD = L, P'A \cdot DP = K, AC \cdot PD = M, AP' \cdot DC = N$. J, K, L are to be shown to be collinear. Since lines PA, PB, PC, PD $\overline{\wedge}$ lines $P'A$, $P'B$, $P'C$, $P'D$, sections of these lines are also projectively related (Def. 3.53). Therefore $AJMC \overline{\wedge} NLDC$ and since C corresponds to itself we have a perspectivity (Theorem 3.83). But $AN \cdot MD = K$ and hence JL goes through K. The proof of the converse is left to the student.

THEOREM 3.92   *A point conic is uniquely determined by five distinct points, no three of which are collinear.*

Let the five points be P, P', A, B, C and let D be any sixth point on the conic generated by projective pencils through P and P' and the points A, B, C. Then diagonal points of hexagon $PBP'ACD$ are collinear. (Note that the first and third points of the hexagon are the points containing the projective pencils.) But hexagon $PBP'ACD$ is the same as hexagons $BP'ACDP$, $P'ACDPB$, etc. Hence the points P', C, D, P are on the point conic generated by projective pencils through A and B; points A, D, P, B are on the point conic generated by projective pencils through P' and C, etc. Thus, if D is on the conic determined by pencils through P, P' and the points A, B, C, it is also on the conic determined by pencils through A, B and points P', C, P, and on the conic determined by pencils through P', C and points A, P, B, etc. Thus the conic containing the five given points is unique and may be generated by a projectivity between the pencils through any two of its points.

As a consequence of Theorem 3.92 we have the "Mystic Hexagram" theorem proven by Pascal (1623–1662) in 1640:

THEOREM 3.93 *If the vertices of a hexagon are points of a point conic, its diagonal points are collinear.*

The proof follows that of Theorem 3.91 where, due to Theorem 3.92, any two of the vertices may be taken as the points containing the projective pencils.

The line determined by the hexagon in Pascal's theorem is called the *Pascal line* for the hexagon. From a given set of six points 60 different hexagons may be formed and thus 60 Pascal lines determined. This configuration has many interesting properties, for which the student is referred to Eves, p.82.

COROLLARY 1 *If a pentagon ABCDE is inscribed in a conic, the three points $AB \cdot DE$, $BC \cdot EA$, $CD \cdot$ tangent at A, are collinear.*

(The proof is similar to that of Theorem 3.91. Consider hexagon $AABCDE$ where line AA denotes the tangent at A.)

COROLLARY 2 *If ABCD is a quadrangle inscribed in a conic, the four points $AB \cdot CD$, $AC \cdot BD$, tangent at B $\cdot$ tangent at C, and tangent at A $\cdot$ tangent at D, are collinear.*

(The proof is similar to that of Theorem 3.91. Consider hexagons $ABBDCC$ and $AABDDC$ where AA, BB, CC, DD denote tangents at A, B, C, D, respectively.)

The student should now dualize this entire section. It can be shown that the set of tangents to a point conic is a line conic. We will show this later (Sec. 5.6). The dual of Pascal's theorem was discovered independently by Brianchon in 1806 in the form "If a hexagon is circumscribed about a conic, the lines joining its opposite vertices are concurrent."

1. Prove the converse of Theorem 3.91.

2. Prove Corollary 1 of Theorem 3.93.

3. Prove Corollary 2 of Theorem 3.93.

4. Given five points, no three of which are collinear, draw at any one of them the tangent to the conic determined by the five points.

5. Prove that if a triangle is inscribed in a conic, then the tangents at the vertices intersect the opposite sides in three collinear points. (Show that the inscribed triangle and the circumscribed triangle formed by the tangents are Desarguesean.)

6. Dualize all the definitions and theorems of Section 3.9. (The dual of *tangent* is *point of contact*.)

3.10   Coordinates in the Real Projective Plane

We end this chapter by setting up a system of coordinates in the real projective plane as an extension of the coordinates on a line set up in Section 3.7.

Let X, Y, Z, U be four arbitrary points no three of which are collinear (Fig. 3.10 1). Let U_y and U_x be points on ZX and ZY such that $U_x = YU \cdot ZX$ and $U_y = XU \cdot ZY$. Let coordinates on lines ZX and ZY be deter-

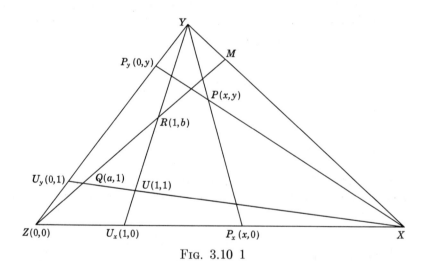

Fig. 3.10 1

mined by points Z, U_x, X and Z, U_y, Y as follows: On ZX we assign to Z, U_x, X the symbols 0, 1, ∞, respectively; on ZY we assign the symbols 0, 1, ∞ to Z, U_y, Y. Then, through the nets of rationality thus determined we obtain coordinates for the points on each line as in Sec. 3.7. For any point P in the plane, not on line XY, we then obtain the coordinates (x, y), where x is the coordinate of $P_x = YP \cdot ZX$, and y is the coordinate of $P_y =$

$XP \cdot ZY$. Note that U has coordinates $(1, 1)$; any point R, other than Y, on line YU_x has its first coordinate equal to 1; and any point Q, other than X, on line XU_y has its second coordinate equal to 1. Thus every point in the projective plane has a unique pair of real numbers as coordinates except those on line XY for which the above process fails. This exceptional line depends on the choice of the four reference points of the coordinate system. However, we do not wish any line to be exceptional and hence we introduce a new kind of coordinate.

DEFINITION 3.10 1   *Homogeneous coordinates*   On a line we replace the single coordinate x by two coordinates (x_1, x_2) such that $x = x_1/x_2$. The point (kx_1, kx_2) is thus the same as the point (x_1, x_2) for every $k \neq 0$. We say that a ratio a/b is ∞ if and only if $b/a = 0$. The point whose coordinate is ∞ is then represented by $(1,0)$, point 1 by $(1, 1)$, and point 0 by $(0, 1)$. In the plane a point with coordinates (x, y) as previously defined, is represented by the triple (x_1, x_2, x_3) such that $x = x_1/x_3$, and $y = x_2/x_3$; or $x : y : 1 = x_1 : x_2 : x_3$. Hence point (kx_1, kx_2, kx_3) is the same as point (x_1, x_2, x_3) for every $k \neq 0$. These new coordinates are called *homogeneous coordinates* (Fig. 3.10 2).

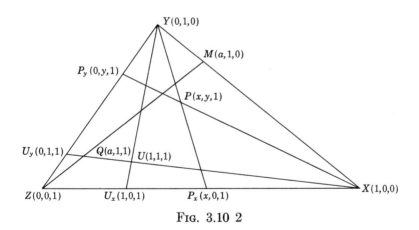

FIG. 3.10 2

If P is any point not on XY and if P has non-homogeneous coordinates (x, y), we can choose $(x, y, 1)$ as homogeneous coordinates for P. Thus point U has coordinates $(1, 1, 1)$ and $Z = (0, 0, 1)$. For a point M on XY we proceed as follows: let $Q = ZM \cdot XU = (a, 1, 1)$, and assign to M the homogeneous coordinates $(a, 1, 0)$. Thus $Y = (0, 1, 0)$ and to X we assign coordinates $(1, 0, 0)$. Now every point in the projective plane has been assigned a triple of real numbers where point $(x_1, x_2, x_3) = (kx_1, kx_2, kx_3)$ for all $k \neq 0$; and any triple of real numbers except $(0, 0, 0)$ represents a unique point relative to the *triangle of reference XYZ* and unit point *U*.

Note that the three lines of the triangle of reference *XYZ* divide the projective plane into four regions where the homogeneous coordinates of the points have signs as shown in Fig. 3.10 3, depending on the position of *U*.

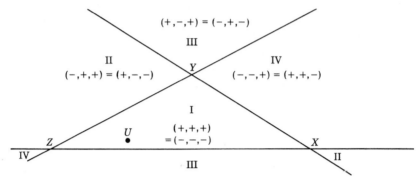

FIG. 3.10 3

We now have a basis for analytic projective geometry. We shall, however, consider this from a different point of view in Chapter 5.

Exercises

1. Give three sets of homogeneous coordinates for each of the points whose non-homogeneous coordinates are: (a) (1, 2), (b) (1/2, 3), (c) (−2, 0), (d) (−2/3, −1/4), (e) (5, −2).

2. Give the non-homogeneous coordinates for each of the points whose homogeneous coordinates are: (a) (1, 2, 3), (b) (2, 4, 6), (c) (1, 0, −2), (d) (0, −3, 1), (e) (2, −1, 0).

References

Adler, Chap. 7, 8, 9; Coxeter (1), Chap. 2; Coxeter (3), Chap. 14; Fishback, Chap. 10; Meserve, Chaps. 2, 3; Seidenberg, Chaps. II, IV, VI; Young (2), Chaps. III, IV, V.

PART II

GEOMETRY AS THE STUDY OF THE
INVARIANT THEORY OF A TRANSFORMATION GROUP

CHAPTER 4

INTRODUCTION: KLEIN'S
ERLANGER PROGRAMM

In a lecture given in 1872 on his appointment to a professorship at the University of Erlangen, Felix Klein (1849–1925) presented a definition of geometry which introduced order into the mass of geometric information existing at the time. Before giving this definition however, we introduce briefly some necessary underlying concepts.

4.1 Transformations

DEFINITION 4.11 A *transformation* T of a set A onto a set B is a one-to-one correspondence between the elements of A and those of B. If a is an element of A and b is the corresponding element of B, we write $T(a) = b$ (or $a \rightarrow b$) and say that b corresponds to a under T(or that a is transformed into b). The perspectivities and projectivities of Sec. 3.5 are examples of transformations.

DEFINITION 4.12 The *inverse* T^{-1} of a transformation T is a transformation of set B onto set A such that if $T(a) = b$, then $T^{-1}(b) = a$, where a is an element of A and b is an element of B.

DEFINITION 4.13 If T_1 is a transformation of set A onto set B and T_2 is a transformation of set B onto set C, then the transformation T_2T_1, obtained by performing T_1 and then T_2, is a transformation of set A onto set C and is called the *product* of T_1 and T_2. In symbols we write: If $T_1(a) = b$ and $T_2(b) = c$, then $T_2T_1(a) = T_2[T_1(a)] = T_2(b) = c$.

DEFINITION 4.14 For our purposes we shall be interested in the transformations of a set S onto itself. In this case if an element s of S corresponds to itself under a transformation T, then s is called an *invariant* element or a *fixed* element of S under T. If a transformation leaves every element of S fixed, it is called the *identity* transformation and is denoted by I.

As illustrations of these concepts, let set S be the set of points of a Euclidean plane on which a Cartesian coordinate system has been set up, and let T_1 be the transformation under which the point $P(x, y)$ is transformed into point $P'(x', y')$ where $x' = x + 2$ and $y' = y - 1$. We will refer to this pair of equations as the transformation T_1. The inverse T_1^{-1} is then the transformation $x' = x - 2, y' = y + 1$. If A is the point $(2, 3)$, then $A' = T_1(A)$ is the point $(4, 2)$. By direct substitution in the equations for T_1^{-1} we see that $T_1^{-1}(A') = A$. We note that T_1, which the student will recognize as a translation, has no fixed or invariant points. If, however, we take a second point $B(1, -3)$ and its corresponding point $B' = T_1(B) = (3, -4)$, we see that the Euclidean distances AB and $A'B'$ are equal. In fact simple substitution will show that for any two points $P_1(x_1, y_1)$ and $P_2(x_2, y_2)$ the Euclidean distance P_1P_2 is equal to the distance $P_1'P_2'$ where $P_1' = T_1(P_1)$ and $P_2' = T_1(P_2)$; i.e., the relation $[(x_2 - x_1)^2 + (y_2 - y_1)^2]^{1/2}$ is invariant under T_1.

Now let T_2 be the transformation $x' = 2x, y' = y$. Then T_2^{-1} is the transformation $x' = x/2, y' = y$. T_2 has a fixed point, namely $(0, 0)$. Euclidean distance is *not* invariant under T_2 as can be seen by comparing the distance between $A(2, 3)$ and $B(1, -3)$ with the distance between $T_2(A)$ and $T_2(B)$.

The transformation T_1 is an example of a Euclidean *motion;* i.e., a transformation which keeps Euclidean distance invariant. Whereas Euclid tacitly assumed that motion without deformation was possible and used superposition to define congruence, it is the concept of transformation that will be used in Chapter 6 to define Euclidean motion and yield a rigorous definition of congruence.

Working out the product of the two transformations above we see that $T_2T_1(A)$ is the point $(8, 2)$ but $T_1T_2(A)$ is the point $(6, 2)$. Hence $T_1T_2 \neq T_2T_1$. In fact T_2T_1 is the transformation $x' = 2(x + 2) = 2x + 4, y' = y - 1$; while T_1T_2 is the transformation $x' = 2x + 2, y' = y - 1$. Thus we see that multiplication of transformations is not necessarily commutative.

The following theorems are immediate consequences of the definitions of this section. In each we assume that the transformations involved are those of a set S onto itself.

Theorem 4.11 $TT^{-1} = T^{-1}T = I$.

Theorem 4.12 $TI = IT = T$.

Theorem 4.13   *Multiplication is associative:* $T_1(T_2T_3) = (T_1T_2)T_3$.

Theorem 4.14   *If $T_1T_2 = I$, then $T_2 = T_1^{-1}$.*

Exercises

1. Prove Theorem 4.11.

2. Prove Theorem 4.12.

3. Prove Theorem 4.13.

4. Prove Theorem 4.14.

5. If S is the set of all the points in the Euclidean plane, T_1 is a translation of one unit to the right, and T_2 is a rotation of $90°$ about a fixed point O, does $T_2T_1 = T_1T_2$? Show your work.

6. Given $T_1 : x' = x - 3$, $y' = y + 2$;
$$T_2 : x' = -y,\ y' = x.$$
Find (a) T_2T_1, (b) T_1T_2, (c) $T_1{}^{-1}$, (d) $T_2{}^{-1}$, (e) $T_1{}^2$, (f) $T_2{}^2$, (g) $(T_2T_1)^{-1}$, (h) $T_1{}^{-1}T_2{}^{-1}$.

7. Do Ex. 6 for $T_1 : x' = 2x - y$, $y' = x + y$; $T_2 : x' = 3x + y$, $y' = x - 2y$.

4.2 Transformation Groups

DEFINITION 4.21 A set of transformations of a set S onto itself forms a *transformation group* if it contains (1) the inverse of every transformation of the set, and (2) the product of any two transformations of the set. As a consequence of this definition every group of transformations of a set S onto itself contains the identity transformation I.

DEFINITION 4.22 A property which is unchanged under all the transformations of a group is called an *invariant* of the group.

DEFINITION 4.23 If the transformations in a subset of a given group G form a group, the subset is called a *subgroup* of G. Every invariant of a given group of transformations is an invariant of every subgroup of the given group.

As an illustration, consider the set S of points on a real projective line on which a homogeneous coordinate system has been set up, so that each point P has real homogeneous coordinates (x_1, x_2). Let the set G of transformations be given by

$$T : x_1' = ax_1 + bx_2, \quad x_2' = cx_1 + dx_2$$

where the coefficients a, b, c, d may have any real values subject to the condition that the determinant

$$\Delta = \begin{vmatrix} a & b \\ c & d \end{vmatrix} \neq 0.$$

We wish to show that this set of transformations forms a group. (In the following, an elementary knowledge of square matrices and determinants of order 2 is assumed).

For condition (1) of Def. 4.21: We solve for T^{-1} and find it to be

$$T^{-1} : x_1' = (dx_1 - bx_2)/\Delta, \quad x_2' = (-cx_1 + ax_2)/\Delta.$$

We see that the coefficients are real numbers and that their determinant is

$$\frac{1}{\Delta^2} \begin{vmatrix} d & -b \\ -c & a \end{vmatrix} = 1/\Delta \neq 0.$$

Thus the inverse of every transformation in G is also in G.

For condition (2) of Def. 4.21: Take any two transformations in G

$$T_1 : x_1' = ax_1 + bx_2,\ x_2' = cx_1 + dx_2;\ \ \Delta_1 = \begin{vmatrix} a & b \\ c & d \end{vmatrix} \neq 0$$

$$T_2 : x_1' = ex_1 + fx_2,\ x_2' = gx_1 + hx_2;\ \ \Delta_2 = \begin{vmatrix} e & f \\ g & h \end{vmatrix} \neq 0.$$

Then T_2T_1 is given by

$$x_1' = e(ax_1 + bx_2) + f(cx_1 + dx_2) = (ea + fc)x_1 + (eb + fd)x_2$$
$$x_2' = g(ax_1 + bx_2) + h(cx_1 + dx_2) = (ga + hc)x_1 + (gb + hd)x_2.$$

The coefficients of T_2T_1 are real numbers and their determinant is the product $\Delta_2\Delta_1$ and hence $\neq 0$.

We call the matrix $\begin{bmatrix} a & b \\ c & d \end{bmatrix}$ the matrix of transformation T_1 and the matrix $\begin{bmatrix} e & f \\ g & h \end{bmatrix}$ the matrix of transformation T_2. We note that the matrix of T_2T_1 is the product of the matrix of T_2 by the matrix of T_1, and that the matrix of T^{-1} is the inverse of the matrix of T. It should also be noted that in this illustration, since we are dealing with homogeneous coordinates, the point $(\Delta \cdot x_1, \Delta \cdot x_2)$ is the same as the point (x_1, x_2) and hence the matrix of T^{-1} may be taken simply as $\begin{bmatrix} d & -b \\ -c & a \end{bmatrix}$; i.e., T^{-1} is given by

$$T^{-1} : x_1' = dx_1 - bx_2,\ \ x_2' = -cx_1 + ax_2.$$

Some transformation groups contain only a finite number of transformations. Such a group is called a *finite group*. For example: Let S be the set of points in a Euclidean plane which are on a given equilateral triangle ABC

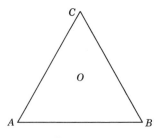

FIG. 4.21

(Fig. 4.21). Let O be the center of the triangle and let the following transformations have the usual Euclidean definitions:

T_1 : Rotation of 120° about O; i.e., $T_1(A, B, C) = B, C, A$.
T_2 : Rotation of 240° about O; i.e., $T_2(A, B, C) = C, A, B$.
T_3 : Reflection in the median from A; i.e., $T_3(A, B, C) = A, C, B$.
T_4 : Reflection in the median from B; i.e., $T_4(A, B, C) = C, B, A$.
T_5 : Reflection in the median from C; i.e., $T_5(A, B, C) = B, A, C$.
I : The identity transformation; i.e., $I(A, B, C) = A, B, C$.

These transformations all transform the equilateral triangle into itself. To find the product of any two of these transformations we find the transforms of A, B, C. Thus

$$T_2 T_1(A, B, C) = T_2(B, C, A) = A, B, C. \text{ Therefore } T_2 T_1 = I.$$

$$T_3 T_1(A, B, C) = T_3(B, C, A) = C, B, A. \text{ Therefore } T_3 T_1 = T_4.$$

In this way it can be shown that the product of any two of the transformations of the set is in the set. Also each transformation has an inverse in the set; e.g., $T_2^{-1} = T_1$. This group of transformations is the group of *symmetries of the equilateral triangle*.

Exercises

1. (a) Show that the following four transformations form a group:

$$T_1 : x' = -x, \, y' = y; \qquad T_2 : x' = x, \, y' = -y;$$
$$T_3 : x' = -x, \, y' = -y; \qquad T_4 : x' = x, \, y' = y.$$

(b) Show that each of the following pairs of transformations forms a subgroup of (a): T_1 and T_4, T_2 and T_4, T_3 and T_4.

2. Show that the set of all projectivities of a line onto itself forms a group. (The harmonic relation is an invariant of this group).

3. Show that the set of translations in the Euclidean plane given by the equations $x' = x + h$, $y' = y + k$, where h and k are real numbers, forms a group; and show that the Euclidean distance between two points is an invariant of this group.

4. Do Ex. 3 for the set of rotations: $x' = x \cos \theta - y \sin \theta$, $y' = x \sin \theta + y \cos \theta$.

5. Show that the set of transformations given by equations $x' = x \cos \theta + y \sin \theta$, $y' = x \sin \theta - y \cos \theta$, does not form a group.

6. Show that the set of transformations on a projective line given by $x' = (ax + b)/(cx + d)$, where a, b, c, d are real numbers and where $ad - bc \neq 0$, forms a group. (Note that the point $x = -d/c$ corresponds to $x' = \infty$. Solving for x shows that if $x = \infty$, $x' = a/c$.)

7. Show that the set of transformations given by equations $x' = ax + b$, $y' = y/a + d$, where b and d are any real numbers and $a > 0$, forms a group.

8. Complete the proof that the six symmetries of the equilateral triangle form a group.

9. What is the group of symmetries of an isosceles triangle? Of a rectangle?

10. Let S be the set of points in the Euclidean plane on which a rectangular coordinate system has been set up, and let the following transformations have their usual Euclidean definitions;

T_1 : A rotation of 90° about the origin.
T_2 : A rotation of 180° about the origin.
T_3 : A rotation of 270° about the origin.
T_4 : A reflection in the x-axis.
T_5 : A reflection in the y-axis.
T_6 : A reflection in the line $x = y$.
T_7 : A reflection in the line $x = -y$.
I : The identity transformation.

Write out a multiplication table for these transformations, and show that they form a group. Show that the four points $(\pm 1, \pm 1)$ form an invariant set (not pointwise invariant) under this group. This group is the group of symmetries of a square.

4.3   Klein's *Erlanger Programm*

We are now ready for Klein's famous definition of a geometry:

A geometry is the study of those properties of a set S which remain invariant when the elements of S are subjected to the transformations of some transformation group.

Thus, from this point of view, we again have the way opened for new geometries. We need only choose a fundamental element (e.g., point, line, circle), a space or set S of these elements (e.g., plane of points, a spherical surface of points, a plane of lines, a pencil of circles), and finally a group of transformations to which the fundamental elements are to be subjected. Then the definitions and theorems of the geometry consist of the properties invariant under the group of transformations.

In the next three chapters we shall consider projective geometry from Klein's point of view and show that Euclidean geometry, the two non-Euclidean geometries of Chapter 1, and other geometries are subgeometries of projective geometry.

References

Adler, Chap. 11; Eves, Chaps. III and IX; Levy, Chap. I.

CHAPTER 5

LINEAR TRANSFORMATIONS: PROJECTIVE GEOMETRY

5.1 Analytic Model of the Real Projective Plane

Models of abstract axiom systems were discussed in Chapter 2. The student no doubt recognized that Ex. 9 at the end of that chapter indicated a means of forming an analytic model for the Euclidean plane. "Analytic Geometry" is thus not a geometry but a method; i.e., one can study properties of the Euclidean plane by means of an analytic model.

We now proceed to create an analytic model of the real projective plane. In what follows, an elementary knowledge of matrices of order two and three is assumed, as is also a knowledge of solutions of sets of linear equations in two or three variables.

DEFINITIONS 5.11 A *point* in the real projective plane is a class of real ordered number triples, called *homogeneous coordinates* of the point, denoted by (x_1, x_2, x_3), where $(0, 0, 0)$ is excluded and where two ordered number triples (x_1, x_2, x_3) and (y_1, y_2, y_3) are in the same class (i.e., represent the same point) if and only if $y_i = kx_i$, $k \neq 0$. A *line* is defined also as a real ordered number triple but shall be denoted by $[u_1, u_2, u_3]$, where $[0, 0, 0]$ is excluded and where $[u_1, u_2, u_3]$ and $[v_1, v_2, v_3]$ are in the same class (i.e., represent the same line) if and only if $v_i = ku_i$, $k \neq 0$. A point (x_1, x_2, x_3) and a line $[u_1, u_2, u_3]$ are *incident* if and only if $u_1x_1 + u_2x_2 + u_3x_3 = 0$. (Note duality.) Therefore the linear homogeneous equation $u_1x_1 + u_2x_2 + u_3x_3 = 0$ may be considered to be the *point equation* of the line $[u_1, u_2, u_3]$ or the *line equation* of the point (x_1, x_2, x_3).

The point equation of a line represents the pencil of points on the line, while the line equation of a point represents the pencil of lines through the point. For example, $3x_1 + 2x_2 + 4x_3 = 0$ represents the pencil of points on the line $[3, 2, 4]$, while $3u_1 + 2u_2 + 4u_3 = 0$ represents the pencil of lines through the point $(3, 2, 4)$. (For finite projective planes we limit the field over which the x_i and the u_i vary to a finite field. See, for example, the analytic model for the seven-point geometry of Sec. 2.10 in Meserve, pp. 18–20).

DEFINITION 5.12 The points $X(1, 0, 0)$, $Y(0, 1, 0)$, $Z(0, 0, 1)$ will be called the *vertices of the triangle of reference;* the point $U(1, 1, 1)$ will be called the *unit point* (cf. Sec. 3.10).

We must now show that the axioms for the real projective plane are satisfied by the points and lines as defined above. We start with the axioms of incidence which, for convenience, we reproduce here.

Axiom 1: There exist a point and a line that are not incident.

Axiom 2: Every line is incident with at least three points.

Axiom 3: Any two distinct points are incident with one and only one line.

Axiom 4: Any two distinct lines are incident with at least one point.

The first two axioms are easily seen to be satisfied: For Axiom 1, we need merely exhibit two triples of numbers (x_1, x_2, x_3) and $[u_1, u_2, u_3]$ such that $u_1 x_1 + u_2 x_2 + u_3 x_3 \neq 0$; for Axiom 2, we must show that for any given triple $[u_1, u_2, u_3]$ we can find at least three distinct triples (x_1, x_2, x_3) such that $u_1 x_1 + u_2 x_2 + u_3 x_3 = 0$.

For Axiom 3: Let the given points be $A(a_1, a_2, a_3)$ and $B(b_1, b_2, b_3)$. We are looking for a line $[u_1, u_2, u_3]$ such that

$$u_1 a_1 + u_2 a_2 + u_3 a_3 = 0$$

and

$$u_1 b_1 + u_2 b_2 + u_3 b_3 = 0.$$

From the theory of sets of linear homogeneous equations we know that this pair of equations has non-trivial solutions given by

$$u_1 : u_2 : u_3 = \begin{vmatrix} a_2 & a_3 \\ b_2 & b_3 \end{vmatrix} : \begin{vmatrix} a_3 & a_1 \\ b_3 & b_1 \end{vmatrix} : \begin{vmatrix} a_1 & a_2 \\ b_1 & b_2 \end{vmatrix}$$

so that if a particular triple, u_1, u_2, u_3, is a solution, all other solutions are given by ku_1, ku_2, ku_3. But the line $[ku_1, ku_2, ku_3]$ is the same as the line $[u_1, u_2, u_3]$. Hence we have a unique line containing A and B and we may choose $[u_1, u_2, u_3] = \left[\begin{vmatrix} a_2 & a_3 \\ b_2 & b_3 \end{vmatrix}, \begin{vmatrix} a_3 & a_1 \\ b_3 & b_1 \end{vmatrix}, \begin{vmatrix} a_1 & a_2 \\ b_1 & b_2 \end{vmatrix} \right]$ which the student should show $\neq [0, 0, 0]$.

By the duality of the definitions of point and line in our model, Axiom 4, together with Theorem 3.21, is verified in the same way as Axiom 3.

THEOREM 5.11   *The equation of the line determined by points $A(a_1, a_2, a_3)$ and $B(b_1, b_2, b_3)$ may be expressed in the form:*

$$\begin{vmatrix} x_1 & x_2 & x_3 \\ a_1 & a_2 & a_3 \\ b_1 & b_2 & b_3 \end{vmatrix} = 0.$$

This follows from the value for $[u_1, u_2, u_3]$ found in the course of verifying Axiom 3 above. Dually, the equation of the point of intersection of the lines $[a_1, a_2, a_3]$ and $[b_1, b_2, b_3]$ is

$$\begin{vmatrix} u_1 & u_2 & u_3 \\ a_1 & a_2 & a_3 \\ b_1 & b_2 & b_3 \end{vmatrix} = 0.$$

COROLLARY   *Three distinct points are collinear if and only if the determinant of their homogeneous coordinates is equal to 0; dually, three distinct lines are concurrent if and only if the determinant of their homogeneous coordinates is equal to 0.*

THEOREM 5.12   *If $A(a_1, a_2, a_3)$ and $B(b_1, b_2, b_3)$ are two distinct points, any point P of the pencil of points determined by A and B is given by $P(p_1, p_2, p_3)$ where $p_i = \lambda_2 a_i + \lambda_1 b_i$, $i = 1, 2, 3$, and λ_1 and λ_2 are real but not both equal to 0.*

The proof consists of two parts. First we must show that the coordinates of P, as given, satisfy the equation of line AB as given in Theorem 5.11. This we leave to the student. We shall now show that if a triple of real numbers $(p_1, p_2, p_3) \neq (0, 0, 0)$ does satisfy the condition

$$\begin{vmatrix} p_1 & p_2 & p_3 \\ a_1 & a_2 & a_3 \\ b_1 & b_2 & b_3 \end{vmatrix} = 0,$$

then there exist two real numbers λ_1 and λ_2, not both zero, such that $\lambda_2 a_i + \lambda_1 b_i = p_i$, $i = 1, 2, 3$. This represents three equations in two variables for which a unique solution exists under the hypotheses above.

Dually, if $m[m_1, m_2, m_3]$ and $n[n_1, n_2, n_3]$ are two distinct lines, any line p of the pencil of lines determined by m and n is given by $p[p_1, p_2, p_3]$, where $p_i = \mu_2 m_i + \mu_1 n_i$, $i = 1, 2, 3$, and μ_1 and μ_2 are real and not both equal to zero.

DEFINITION 5.13 The above method of representing the elements of a pencil is called the *parametric* method and the points A and B are called *base points*.

Since point (p_1, p_2, p_3) is the same as point (kp_1, kp_2, kp_3), we may multiply λ_1 and λ_2 of Theorem 5.12 by any real, nonzero number, but the ratio $\lambda = \lambda_1/\lambda_2$ remains the same. In terms of λ the coordinates of a point P on line AB may be written as $p_i = a_i + \lambda b_i$, $i = 1, 2, 3$. We say that the point P corresponds to the parameter $\lambda = \lambda_1/\lambda_2$, and we refer to (λ_1, λ_2) as *homogeneous parameters of P with respect to the base points A and B.* We say that $\lambda = \infty$ if and only if $\lambda_2 = 0$. From the equations $p_i = \lambda_2 a_i + \lambda_1 b_i$ we note that point A has homogeneous parameters $(0, 1)$ and corresponds to $\lambda = 0$, while B has homogeneous parameters $(1, 0)$ and corresponds to $\lambda = \infty$. Thus λ may be any real number or ∞. To each value of λ there corresponds one point of the pencil and conversely, to each point of the pencil corresponds one value of λ. We therefore speak of *point λ*, with homogeneous parameters (λ_1, λ_2) with respect to base points $A(0, 1)$ and $B(1, 0)$. On a given line any two points may be chosen as the base points. The student should write out the dual of Definition 5.13 and the material following it.

As an illustration, consider the following: $P(-1, 8, 5)$ is a point on the line determined by $A(1, 1, -2)$ and $B(-1, 2, 3)$. We wish to find homogeneous parameters for P with respect to base points A and B; i.e., we seek λ_1 and λ_2 such that

$$\lambda_2 a_i + \lambda_1 b_i = p_i, \quad i = 1, 2, 3.$$

This involves solving the following equations:

$$\lambda_2 - \lambda_1 = -1$$
$$\lambda_2 + 2\lambda_1 = 8$$
$$-2\lambda_2 + 3\lambda_1 = 5.$$

From these we get $\lambda_1 = 3$, $\lambda_2 = 2$ and therefore $\lambda = 3/2$.

THEOREM 5.13 *For points which are on a side of the reference triangle, but which are not vertices, the two non-zero coordinates may be taken as homogeneous parameters with respect to the vertices as base points.*

This follows from Theorem 5.12. For example, on $x_2 = 0$, if we use $Z(0, 0, 1)$ and $X(1, 0, 0)$ as base points, then any point $(x_1, 0, x_3)$ on the line has homogeneous parameters (x_1, x_3).

We now adopt Definition 3.32 and proceed to verify Axiom 5.

Axiom 5: If two triangles are perspective from a point, then they are perspective from a line.

Let the two triangles have vertices $A(a_1, a_2, a_3)$, $B(b_1, b_2, b_3)$, $C(c_1, c_2, c_3)$, and $A'(a_1', a_2', a_3')$, $B'(b_1', b_2', b_3')$, $C'(c_1', c_2', c_3')$ and be perspective from $P(p_1, p_2, p_3)$. Let $AB \cdot A'B' = Q$, $BC \cdot B'C' = R$, and $AC \cdot A'C' = S$ (Fig. 5.11). Since P is on AA', BB', and CC', there exist homogeneous param-

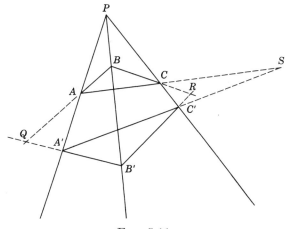

FIG. 5.11

eters (α_1, α_2), (β_1, β_2), (λ_1, λ_2), such that $p_i = \alpha_2 a_i + \alpha_1 a_i' = \beta_2 b_i + \beta_1 b_i' = \lambda_2 c_i + \lambda_1 c_i'$, $i = 1, 2, 3$. Hence $\alpha_2 a_i - \beta_2 b_i = \beta_1 b_i' - \alpha_1 a_i'$, $i = 1, 2, 3$. But by Theorem 5.12, $\alpha_2 a_i - \beta_2 b_i$, $i = 1, 2, 3$, are coordinates of a point on AB and $\beta_1 b_i' - \alpha_1 a_i'$, $i = 1, 2, 3$, are coordinates of a point on $A'B'$. We may therefore take either triple as coordinates of $AB \cdot A'B' = Q$. We choose $\alpha_2 a_i - \beta_2 b_i$, $i = 1, 2, 3$. Similarly, $\beta_2 b_i - \lambda_2 c_i$, $i = 1, 2, 3$, are coordinates of R, and $\lambda_2 c_i - \alpha_2 a_i$, $i = 1, 2, 3$, are coordinates of S. Evaluation of the determinant of the coordinates of Q, R, S will show that the condition for collinearity in the Corollary to Theorem 5.11 is satisfied.

Axiom 6 may be verified in a similar manner. However, we postpone this to Section 5.5 where a simpler method is suggested.

For the axioms of order we shall need to develop the analytic form for a projectivity, and also find some way of defining separation for our analytic model. We therefore postpone consideration of these axioms until we have developed the necessary preliminaries.

Exercises

1. Complete the proofs that show that the four incidence axioms for a projective plane are satisfied by the analytic model of this section.

2. Show that the point (a, b, c) cannot be on the line $[a, b, c]$.

3. Prove the first part of Theorem 5.12.

4. Finish the proof of the verification of Axiom 5.

5. (a) Find the coordinates of the line joining the points $(0, 2, 1)$ and $(1, 1, 0)$. (b) Find the equation of the line joining the points in (a). (c) Find the points of intersection of the lines whose equations are $2x_2 + x_3 = 0$ and $x_1 + x_2 = 0$. (d) Find the coordinates of the line joining the points whose equations are $2u_2 + u_3 = 0$ and $u_1 + u_2 = 0$.

6. Find the point of intersection of the line joining $(2, 1, 1)$ to $(0, 1, 2)$, and the line $3x_1 - 5x_2 + 2x_3 = 0$.

7. Starting with the four points X, Y, Z, U of Def. 5.12 (cf. Fig. 3.10 2) and the arbitrary point $P(x, y, 1)$, find (a) the coordinates and equations of the following lines: $ZY, ZX, XY, XU, YU, ZU, XP, YP$, and ZQ, where Q is $(a, 1, 1)$; (b) the coordinates of the following points determined as the intersection of the indicated pairs of lines: $P_x = YP \cdot ZX$, $P_y = XP \cdot ZY$, $U_x = YU \cdot ZX$, $U_y = XU \cdot ZY$, $M = ZQ \cdot XY$, $N = ZU \cdot XY$.

8. Under the conditions of Ex. 7, show that if $A(a_1, a_2, a_3)$ is any point distinct from Z, then $ZA \cdot XY = A'(a_1, a_2, 0)$.

9. Under the conditions of Ex. 7, find the points of intersection of line PU with the sides of the reference triangle.

10. Under the conditions of Ex. 7, show that points P' on line ZP, which are not on line XY, have coordinates $(kx, ky, 1)$.

11. Under the conditions of Ex. 7, show that the line U_xU_y and the line joining $(a, 0, 1)$ to $(0, a, 1)$ meet on line XY.

12. Under the conditions of Ex. 7, find the coordinates of $R = XY \cdot U_xU_y$, $S = ZX \cdot NU_y$, $T = ZY \cdot NU_x$. Show that R, S, T are collinear and find the coordinates of this line.

13. Show that each side of the reference triangle has as coordinates the same ordered triple as the coordinates of the vertex not on that side. (The *unit line* $[1, 1, 1]$ is the line RST of Ex. 12.)

14. Show that the points $A(2, 3, -2)$, $B(1, 2, -4)$, $C(0, 1, -6)$ are collinear and find (a) homogeneous parameters of C with respect to base points A and B; (b) homogeneous parameters of B with respect to base points A and C; (c) homogeneous parameters of A with respect to base points C and B.

15. Show that the quadrangle whose vertices are $(1, \pm 1, \pm 1)$ has the vertices of the reference triangle as its diagonal points (Def. 3.41).

5.2   Perspectivities and Projectivities

We adopt Definition 3.52 and derive the analytic form for a projectivity.

Theorem 5.21   *Any projectivity between the elements of two pencils may be represented by an equation of the form*

$$\mu = (a\lambda + b)/(c\lambda + d), \text{ where } a, b, c, d \text{ are real and } ad - bc \neq 0,$$

between the parameters λ and μ of the elements of the pencils.

We start with a perspectivity between a pencil of points and a pencil of lines. Let the base points of the pencil of points be $A(a_1, a_2, a_3)$ and $B(b_1, b_2, b_3)$, and the base lines of the pencil of lines be $m [m_1, m_2, m_3]$ and $n [n_1, n_2, n_3]$. The condition that a point λ of the pencil of points lie on a line μ of the pencil of lines is that

$$(m_1 + \mu n_1)(a_1 + \lambda b_1) + (m_2 + \mu n_2)(a_2 + \lambda b_2) + (m_3 + \mu n_3)(a_3 + \lambda b_3) = 0.$$

This becomes $c\mu\lambda + d\mu - a\lambda - b = 0$, where a, b, c, d have values depending only on the coordinates of the base elements and are real numbers. Solving for μ gives the desired form of the theorem. That $ad - bc \neq 0$ is due to the fact that a perspectivity is a one-to-one correspondence. (The student should show what happens if $ad - bc = 0$). The inverse relation, giving λ in terms of μ is also of the same form. Thus we have the condition that a pencil of points and a pencil of lines be perspective. Since a projectivity is a sequence of perspectivities and since the product of two linear fractional transformations of the above form is also of this form (Sec. 4.2, Ex. 6), the theorem is proven. Note that the two pencils may be two pencils of points (not necessarily on distinct lines), or two pencils of lines (not necessarily through distinct points) or one of each.

COROLLARY   *By proper choice of base elements any projectivity between the elements of two pencils may be expressed in the form* $\mu = k\lambda$, *where k is real and $\neq 0$.*

Choose the base elements so that the element $\lambda = 0$ of one pencil corresponds to the element $\mu = 0$ of the other, and the element $\lambda = \infty$ corresponds to $\mu = \infty$. Now when $\mu = 0$ in the projectivity expressed by

$$\mu = (a\lambda + b)/(c\lambda + d)$$

we have $a\lambda + b = 0$. For this to correspond to $\lambda = 0$ we must have $b = 0$ and $a \neq 0$. Also when $\mu = \infty$ we have $c\lambda + d = 0$, or $\lambda = -d/c$. For this to correspond to $\lambda = \infty$ we must have $c = 0$ and $d \neq 0$. Hence $\mu = a\lambda/d = k\lambda$, $k \neq 0$. This discussion leads us to the *definition* $k \cdot \infty = \infty$ for $k \neq 0$, and in particular $-\infty = \infty$.

As a result of Theorem 5.12 we noted that any point P on a line p has a unique parameter with respect to two given base points A and B whose parameters are 0 and ∞, respectively. We shall call A the *zero point* and B the *ideal point* of the line p (cf. Sec. 3.7). Again we note that any two points of a line may be chosen as zero point and ideal point. We shall denote the parameter of P by x, and the homogeneous parameters of P by (x_1, x_2) so that $x = x_1/x_2$. The homogeneous parameters of the base points A and B are $(0, 1)$ and $(1, 0)$, respectively. If we now take line p', not necessarily distinct from p, and choose a pair of base points A' and B' on it, then any point P' on p' has a unique parameter, which we shall call x' with respect to its base points A' and B'. Then by Theorem 5.21, any projectivity between the points of p and those of p' has the form

(1) $$x' = (ax + b)/(cx + d), \quad ad - bc \neq 0.$$

In terms of the homogeneous parameters this becomes

$$x_1'/x_2' = (ax_1 + bx_2)/(cx_1 + dx_2), \quad ad - bc \neq 0, \quad \text{or}$$

(2) $$\delta x_1' = ax_1 + bx_2, \quad \delta x_2' = cx_1 + dx_2, \quad \delta \neq 0, \quad ad - bc \neq 0.$$

The linear fractional transformation form (1) is called the *non-homogeneous form of the projectivity;* the linear transformation form (2) is called the *homogeneous form of the projectivity.*

The reason for the use of the arbitrary multiplier δ will be made clear by considering the following transformation:

$$x_1' - 2x_1 + 3x_2$$
$$x_2' = 3x_1 + 2x_2.$$

If $P(x_1, x_2)$ is the point $(1, 1)$, then $P'(x_1', x_2')$ is the point $(5, 5)$ which is the same as the point $(1, 1)$. Thus the unit point on line p' corresponds to the unit point on line p. But if we were to substitute $x_1' = 1, x_2' = 1, x_1 = 1, x_2 = 1$ in the equations of the transformation we see that they are not satisfied. However, there exists a value of $\delta \neq 0$ (namely, $\delta = 5$), such that for $x_1' = 1, x_2' = 1, x_1 = 1, x_2 = 1$,

$$\delta x_1' = 2x_1 + 3x_2$$
$$\delta x_2' = 3x_1 + 2x_2.$$

To summarize, we have proven the following theorem:

Theorem 5.22 *A projectivity between the elements of two pencils is a linear transformation of their homogeneous parameters.*

Corollary 1 *If under a projectivity between the points of lines p and p', the base points $A(0, 1), B(1, 0)$ of p correspond to base points $A'(0, 1), B'(1, 0)$ of p', then the projectivity has the form $\delta x_1' = ax_1, \delta x_2' = dx_2, ad \neq 0$; or the non-homogeneous form $x' = kx, k \neq 0$ (cf. Cor. to Th. 5.21).*

Corollary 2 *If under a projectivity between the points of lines p and p', the base points $A(0, 1), B(1, 0)$ of p correspond respectively to base points $B'(1, 0), A'(0, 1)$ of p', then the projectivity has the form $\delta x_1' = bx_2, \delta x_2' = cx_1, bc \neq 0$. In non-homogeneous form this means that the trans-*

formation $x' = k/x$, $k \neq 0$, *transforms point* ∞ *into point* 0. *This leads us to define* $k/\infty = 0$ *for* k *real and* $\neq 0$.

DEFINITION 5.21 The matrix $\begin{bmatrix} a & b \\ c & d \end{bmatrix}$ is called the *matrix of the transformation* (2). It will be denoted by **A**. Since only ratios are involved any matrix $k\mathbf{A}$, where k is real and not zero, is also a matrix of the same transformation.

If we let X' be the column matrix $\begin{bmatrix} x_1' \\ x_2' \end{bmatrix}$ and **X** be matrix $\begin{bmatrix} x_1 \\ x_2 \end{bmatrix}$ we see that the transformation (2) may be represented by the equation $\delta\mathbf{X}' = \mathbf{A}\mathbf{X}$, $\delta \neq 0$, $\det \mathbf{A} \neq 0$. The inverse transformation T^{-1} is given by $\delta\mathbf{X}' = \mathbf{A}^{-1}\mathbf{X}$. If $\delta\mathbf{X}' = \mathbf{A}\mathbf{X}$ is a projectivity between the points on line p and points on line p', and if $\delta\mathbf{X}'' = \mathbf{B}\mathbf{X}'$ is a projectivity between points on p' and points on p'', then $\delta\mathbf{X}'' = \mathbf{B}\mathbf{A}\mathbf{X}$ is a projectivity between points on p and points on p'' (cf. illustration of Sec. 4.2). The lines p, p', p'' are not necessarily distinct lines.

In what follows we shall refer to the point whose homogeneous parameters are (x_1, x_2) simply as point (x_1, x_2) or point x.

THEOREM 5.23 *For a given choice of parameterization on lines p and p', there exists a unique linear transformation that transforms any three distinct points $E(e_1, e_2)$, $F(f_1, f_2)$, $G(g_1, g_2)$ on p into any three distinct points $Q(q_1, q_2)$, $R(r_1, r_2)$, $S(s_1, s_2)$ on p'.*

Let $A(0, 1)$ and $B(1, 0)$ be the base points on p and let C be the point $(1, 1)$ on p. We show first that there exists a unique linear transformation T_1 that will transform points A, B, C into points E, F, G, respectively. Let T_1 be given by

$$\delta x_1' = ax_1 + bx_2$$
$$ad - bc \neq 0.$$
$$\delta x_2' = cx_1 + dx_2$$

We seek values of a, b, c, d, δ_1, δ_2, δ_3 (since the factor δ may have different values for different pairs of points) such that the following six equations hold:

$$\delta_1 e_1 = b, \qquad \delta_2 f_1 = a, \qquad \delta_3 g_1 = a + b.$$
$$\delta_1 e_2 = d, \qquad \delta_2 f_2 = c, \qquad \delta_3 g_2 = c + d.$$

Since only ratios are involved and none of the δ's is zero, we may assign to one of the δ's, say δ_3, the value 1. This gives us a system of six linear equations in six unknowns which the student can show has a unique set of solutions. The student should also show that $ad - bc \neq 0$. We thus have $T_1(A, B, C) = (E, F, G)$. Therefore $T_1^{-1}(E, F, G) = (A, B, C)$. In a similar manner we show the existence of a unique transformation T_2 such that $T_2(A, B, C) = (Q, R, S)$. Hence our required transformation $T = T_2 T_1^{-1}$.

THEOREM 5.24 *Every linear transformation between the points of two lines is a projectivity* (converse of Th. 5.22).

This follows from Theorem 5.23, Theorem 3.53 (whose proof depends only on axioms already verified in our model), and Theorem 5.22.

COROLLARY *There exists a unique projectivity that transforms any three distinct points on a line p into any three distinct points on a line p', where p' is not necessarily distinct from p.*

Exercises

1. In Theorem 5.21, show that if $ad - bc = 0$ then the correspondence is not one-to-one.
2. In the illustration above Theorem 5.22, show that $(1, -1)$ on p' corresponds to $(1, -1)$ on p.
3. Prove the corollaries to Theorem 5.22.
4. Complete the proof of Theorem 5.23.
5. Find the projectivity which transforms points $(0, 1)$, $(1, 1)$, $(1, 0)$ on p into $(1, 1)$, $(1, 0)$, $(0, 1)$, respectively, on p'.
6. Find the projectivity T which transforms $(0, 1)$, $(1, 0)$ and $(1, 1)$ on p into $(1, 2)$, $(2, 3)$ and $(-1, 0)$, respectively, on p'. Find $T(3, 2)$.
7. Find the projectivity which transforms points $(2, 1)$, $(-1, 4)$ and $(3, 2)$ on p into $(8, 3)$, $(-22, 3)$ and $(2, 1)$, respectively, on p'.

5.3 Cross-ratio of Four Elements in a Pencil

We shall define separation in terms of a fundamental projective property of four elements in a pencil. In what follows we use four points on a line. The student should write out the duals of all definitions and theorems to apply to four lines through a point.

DEFINITION 5.31 If A, B, C, D are four distinct collinear points whose homogeneous parameters are (a_1, a_2), (b_1, b_2), (c_1, c_2), (d_1, d_2), respectively, then the *cross-ratio* of the four points, in the stated order, is the number given by

$$R(A, B, C, D) = \frac{\begin{vmatrix} c_1 & c_2 \\ a_1 & a_2 \end{vmatrix}}{\begin{vmatrix} c_1 & c_2 \\ b_1 & b_2 \end{vmatrix}} \div \frac{\begin{vmatrix} d_1 & d_2 \\ a_1 & a_2 \end{vmatrix}}{\begin{vmatrix} d_1 & d_2 \\ b_1 & b_2 \end{vmatrix}}.$$

In non-homogeneous parameters this becomes

$$R(A, B, C, D) = \frac{(c - a)}{(c - b)} \div \frac{(d - a)}{(d - b)}.$$

We now consider some properties of the cross-ratio. The first three theorems below follow by direct substitution in the definition above in either its homogeneous or its non-homogeneous form.

THEOREM 5.31   *If four distinct points on a line are named in a stated order and if two pairs of points are then interchanged, the value of the cross-ratio is unchanged; i.e., if A, B, C, D are four distinct points on a line then $R(A, B, C, D) = R(B, A, D, C) = R(C, D, A, B) = R(D, C, B, A)$.*

THEOREM 5.32   *If four distinct points on a line are named in a stated order, interchanging either the first pair or the second pair changes the cross-ratio k to its reciprocal $1/k$; interchanging either the inner pair or the outer pair changes the cross-ratio k to $1 - k$. Hence the 24 possible cross-ratios of four points on a line fall into six sets of four with values k, $1/k$, $1 - k$, $(k - 1)/k$, $k/(k - 1)$, $1/(1 - k)$.*

THEOREM 5.33   *If A, B, C, D, E are five distinct collinear points, then $R(A, B, C, D) \cdot R(A, B, D, E) = R(A, B, C, E)$.*

THEOREM 5.34   *The cross-ratio of four points on a line is invariant under a projectivity.*

To prove this let the projectivity be given by

$$\begin{aligned} \delta x_1' &= ax_1 + bx_2 \\ \delta x_2' &= cx_1 + dx_2 \end{aligned} \qquad ad - bc \neq 0.$$

Let the four points A, B, C, D have homogeneous parameters as given in Definition 5.31. We wish to prove $R(A, B, C, D) = R(A', B', C', D')$ where $a_1' = aa_1 + ba_2$, $a_2' = ca_1 + da_2$, etc. Consider one of the determinants in the cross-ratio; e.g.,

$$\begin{vmatrix} c_1' & c_2' \\ a_1' & a_2' \end{vmatrix} = \begin{vmatrix} ac_1 + bc_2 & cc_1 + dc_2 \\ aa_1 + ba_2 & ca_1 + da_2 \end{vmatrix} = \begin{vmatrix} c_1 & c_2 \\ a_1 & a_2 \end{vmatrix} \begin{vmatrix} a & c \\ b & d \end{vmatrix}.$$

We see that each determinant in the cross-ratio is multiplied by the same non-zero constant so that $R(A, B, C, D) = R(A', B', C', D')$.

Corollary *If four distinct points A, B, C, D are on a line not containing $Z(0, 0, 1)$ and have homogeneous coordinates in the plane (a_1, a_2, a_3), (b_1, b_2, b_3), (c_1, c_2, c_3), (d_1, d_2, d_3), respectively, then*

$$R(A, B, C, D) = \frac{\begin{vmatrix} c_1 & c_2 \\ a_1 & a_2 \end{vmatrix}}{\begin{vmatrix} c_1 & c_2 \\ b_1 & b_2 \end{vmatrix}} \div \frac{\begin{vmatrix} d_1 & d_2 \\ a_1 & a_2 \end{vmatrix}}{\begin{vmatrix} d_1 & d_2 \\ b_1 & b_2 \end{vmatrix}}.$$

To show this we note that $ZA \cdot XY = A'$ has coordinates $(a_1, a_2, 0)$, $ZB \cdot XY = B'(b_1, b_2, 0)$, $ZC \cdot XY = C'(c_1, c_2, 0)$, $ZD \cdot XY = D'(d_1, d_2, 0)$ (Sec. 5.1 Ex. 8), and that $ABCD \overset{Z}{\wedge} A'B'C'D'$. The corollary then follows from Theorem 5.34 and Theorem 5.13.

Theorem 5.35 *The cross-ratio of four distinct points on a line cannot be 0, 1, or ∞.*

Let the four points be A, B, C, D with non-homogeneous parameters a, b, c, d, respectively. If $R(A, B, C, D) = 0$, then

$$\frac{(c - a)(d - b)}{(c - b)(d - a)} = 0.$$

Therefore either $c = a$ or $d = b$, contrary to the hypothesis. If $R(A, B, C, D) = \infty$, then either $c = b$, or $d = a$, contrary to the hypothesis. If $R(A, B, C, D) = 1$, then $R(A, C, B, D) = 1 - 1 = 0$ (Th. 5.32), which has been shown to be impossible for four distinct points.

This suggests the following definitions:

Definition 5.32 The cross-ratio of four points on a line, when two of them coincide, is given by:

$$R(A, B, C, C) = 1$$
$$R(A, B, C, B) = 0$$
$$R(A, B, C, A) = \infty.$$

Theorem 5.36 *If three distinct collinear points A, B, C and a real number k are given where $k \neq 0$, 1, then there exists a unique point D such that $R(A, B, C, D) = k$.*

We shall prove the theorem for the case where the three given points are $(0, 1)$, $(1, 1)$, and $(1, 0)$. Then since there exists a unique projectivity that transforms these points into any other three collinear points A, B, C (Cor. to

Th. 5.24) and cross-ratio is invariant under a projectivity (Th. 5.34), the theorem will be valid in the general case. Let D be the point $(d, 1)$, where we wish to find d so that

$$\frac{\begin{vmatrix} 1 & 0 \\ 0 & 1 \end{vmatrix}}{\begin{vmatrix} 1 & 0 \\ 1 & 1 \end{vmatrix}} \div \frac{\begin{vmatrix} d & 1 \\ 0 & 1 \end{vmatrix}}{\begin{vmatrix} d & 1 \\ 1 & 1 \end{vmatrix}} = k.$$

This has the unique solution $d = 1/(1 - k)$.

THEOREM 5.37   *If $R(A, B, C, D) = R(P, Q, S, T)$ then there exists a projectivity that will transform A, B, C, D into P, Q, S, T respectively; i.e., $ABCD \barwedge PQST$.*

This is the converse of Theorem 5.34 and is a consequence of Theorems 5.34, 5.36, and the corollary to Theorem 5.24. The proof is left to the student.

We are now ready for a definition of separation in the analytic model of the projective plane, and the verification of the axioms of order (Sec. 3.6).

DEFINITION 5.33   If A, B, C, D are four distinct points on a line, then the pair A, B *separates* the pair C, D if and only if $R(A, B, C, D)$ is negative.

Using the definition of cross-ratio and the properties derived in Theorems 5.31–5.37, the student may now verify the axioms of order which we repeat here for convenience.

Axiom 7: If $AB \,//\, CD$ then A, B, C, D are distinct and collinear, and $BA \,//\, CD$, $AB \,//\, DC$, $BA \,//\, DC$, $CD \,//\, AB$, $CD \,//\, BA$, $DC \,//\, AB$, $DC \,//\, BA$.

Axiom 8: For any four distinct collinear points A, B, C, D, at least two pairs must separate each other; i.e., at least one of the following holds: $AB \,//\, CD$, $AC \,//\, BD$, or $AD \,//\, BC$.

Axiom 9: If $AB \,//\, CD$ and $AC \,//\, BE$, then $AB \,//\, DE$.

Axiom 10: The separation relation is invariant under a perspectivity.

THEOREM 5.38   *Two distinct points A, B divide the other points of line AB into exactly two segments such that if two points P, Q belong to different segments then $AB \,//\, PQ$; while if P, Q belong to the same segment, they do not separate A, B.*

Let S be a point on line AB distinct from A and B. Then for any point X on

AB, either $R(A, B, S, X) < 0$, or $R(A, B, S, X) > 0$, giving exactly two segments AB. Now by Theorem 5.33,

$$R(A, B, S, P) \cdot R(A, B, P, Q) = R(A, B, S, Q).$$

If P and Q are in different segments, the first and third cross-ratios have opposite signs and hence $R(A, B, P, Q) < 0$, giving us $AB \,//\, PQ$. If P and Q are in the same segment, the first and third cross-ratios have the same sign and hence $R(A, B, P, Q) > 0$, so that A and B do not separate P and Q.

Theorem 5.39　If A, B, C, D are four distinct collinear points then $R(A, B, C, D) = -1$ if and only if $H(A, B, C, D)$.

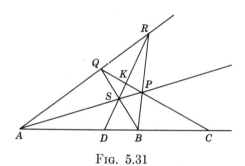

Fig. 5.31

Part I: Given $H(A, B, C, D)$. Let $PQRS$ be a quadrangle yielding $H(A, B, C, D)$ as in Fig. 5.31 (Def. 3.42). Then $ABCD \overset{R}{\underset{\wedge}{=}} QPCK \overset{S}{\underset{\wedge}{=}} BACD$. Therefore $ABCD \overline{\wedge} BACD$ and $R(A, B, C, D) = R(B, A, C, D)$. But if $R(A, B, C, D) = k$, then $R(B, A, C, D) = 1/k$. Therefore $k = 1/k$, $k^2 = 1$ and, since the points are distinct, $k = -1$.

Part II: Given $R(A, B, C, D) = -1$. Let D' be the point such that $H(A, B, C, D')$. Then $R(A, B, C, D') = -1$. But $R(A, B, C, D) = -1$. Hence $D = D'$ (Th. 5.36) and $H(A, B, C, D)$.

We now have one more axiom to verify, Axiom 11 (Sec. 3.7). We must show that there exists an isomorphism between the set of real numbers and all but the point ∞ on the line. But this was done in Theorem 5.12 as explained in the remarks that follow Definition 5.13.

This completes the establishment of the analytic model of the real projective plane. This also serves as a relative consistency proof for the axiom set of Chapter 3. We shall assume that these axioms form a categorical set and shall hereafter study properties of the projective plane both analytically and synthetically.

Exercises

1. Prove Theorem 5.31.

2. Prove Theorem 5.32 and, given $R(A, B, C, D) = k$, write out the 24 possible orders of the four points and their cross-ratios in terms of k.

3. Prove Theorem 5.33.

4. Given collinear points with homogeneous parameters $A(1, 1)$, $B(3, 2)$, $C(1, 0)$ $D(-1, 2)$, find $R(A, B, C, D)$, $R(C, A, B, D)$, $R(D, B, C, A)$, $R(A, C, B, D)$.

5. Given A, B, C as in Ex. 4, find D such that (a) $R(A, B, C, D) = 2$, (b) $R(A, B, C, D) = 1/2$, (c) $R(A, B, C, D) = -1$.

6. Verify by direct calculation that under the transformation $x' = (x + 2)/(x + 1)$, the four points with non-homogeneous parameters 3, 1, 9, 7 are transformed into four points with the same cross-ratio.

7. Show that if, in the unique projectivity that transforms three distinct collinear points A, B, C into points whose homogeneous parameters are $(1, 0)$, $(0, 1)$, $(1, 1)$, respectively, a fourth point D is transformed into $K(k, 1)$, then $R(A, B, C, D) = k$.

8. Show that the points $A(1, 4, 1)$, $B(0, 1, 1)$, $C(2, 3, -3)$ are collinear and find D such that $R(A, B, C, D) = -4$.

9. Find the coordinates of a point D which is collinear with $A(3, 1, 2)$, $B(1, 0, -1)$, $C(1, 1, 4)$ with $R(A, B, C, D) = -2/3$.

10. Find the values of x for which $R(x, 1, 2, 3) = R(1, 2x, 3, 4)$.

11. Determine the orders in which the four numbers 1, 5, 3, 7 may be written so that their cross-ratio is $4/3$.

12. If $R(A, B, C, D) = -1$, evaluate $R(C, A, B, D)$, $R(D, B, C, A)$, $R(A, C, B, D)$, $R(A, C, D, B)$, $R(A, D, B, C)$, $R(D, C, A, B)$.

13. Prove Theorem 5.37.

14. Show that if A and B are base points with respect to which points C and D on line AB have non-homogeneous parameters λ and μ, respectively, then $R(A, B, C, D) = \lambda/\mu$.

15. Write out the duals of the definitions and theorems on cross-ratio.

16. Verify the axioms of order in the analytic model of the real projective plane.

17. The line $x_1 + 2x_2 + 3x_3 = 0$ intersects the sides YZ, ZX, XY, of the reference triangle in points L, M, N, respectively. Let $P = YM \cdot ZN$ and $Q = XP \cdot YZ$. Prove $H(L, Q, Y, Z)$.

18. Given $H(B, C, A, P)$, $H(C, A, P, Q)$, and $H(A, B, Q, R)$. Show that $R(A, P, Q, R) = -2$. (Hint: let A, B, C, have homogeneous parameters $(1, 1)$, $(1, 0)$, $(0, 1)$, respectively).

19. A, B, C, D are four collinear points. C' is the point such that $H(A, B, C, C')$ and D' is the point such that $H(A, B, D, D')$. Prove $R(A, B, C, D) = R(A, B, C', D')$.

20. In Theorem 5.39 we saw that if a particular two of the six possible cross-ratios of four collinear points, namely k and $1/k$, were equal, then the points formed a harmonic set. Investigate the other possible cases of equality of two of the six cross-ratios.

21. State and prove theorems that could be used to replace the corollary to Theorem 5.34 if the 4 points *are* on a line through Z.

22. Verify Theorem 5.39 for the points given in the construction of the net of rationality in Section 3.7.

5.4 Projectivities on a Line

In this section we confine ourselves to points on one line. We assume that two base points have been chosen with respect to which every point on the line has a unique parameter x, where x is a real number or ∞. Each point also has a pair of real homogeneous parameters (x_1, x_2), where $x = x_1/x_2$, $x = \infty$ if and only if $x_2 = 0$, and where $(x_1, x_2) = (kx_1, kx_2)$ for $k \neq 0$ or ∞.

The transformation $T\colon \delta\mathbf{X'} = \mathbf{AX}$, $\delta \neq 0$, $\det \mathbf{A} \neq 0$, represents a projectivity on the line (Sec. 5.2). A projectivity on a line is a linear transformation of a set of points onto itself.

DEFINITION 5.41 If a point on a line corresponds to itself under a projectivity on the line, it is called an *invariant point* or *fixed point* of the projectivity. If a projectivity leaves all points of the line fixed, it is called the *identity projectivity* on the line. Such a projectivity has the matrix

$$\mathbf{I} = \begin{bmatrix} 1 & 0 \\ 0 & 1 \end{bmatrix} \quad \text{or} \quad k\mathbf{I} = \begin{bmatrix} k & 0 \\ 0 & k \end{bmatrix}.$$

THEOREM 5.41 *If a projectivity on a line has three invariant points, it is the identity transformation.* (Proof left to the student).

THEOREM 5.42 *The set of projectivities on a line forms a group.*

(Proof left to the student. See the illustrative example at the end of Sec. 4.2.) Note that the cross-ratio of four elements in a pencil, and hence the separation and harmonic relations are invariants of this group.

THEOREM 5.43 *A projectivity on a line, other than the identity, has two distinct invariant points, two coincident invariant points, or no invariant points.*

Consider first the non-homogeneous form for a projectivity

$$x' = (ax + b)/(cx + d), \quad ad - bc \neq 0.$$

For a point to be invariant we must have $x' = x$. This gives us the quadratic equation

$$cx^2 + (d - a)x - b = 0,$$

whose solutions give the invariant points. There are therefore two distinct invariant points, two coincident invariant points, or no invariant points according as

$$(d - a)^2 + 4bc > 0, \; = 0, \; \text{or} \; < 0.$$

We note that if, in the projectivity of Theorem 5.43, $c = 0$ then the quadratic equation reduces to a linear equation with only one solution. But the expression $(d - a)^2 + 4bc$ becomes $(d - a)^2$ which is >0, indicating that there ought to be two distinct invariant points. This is because one invariant point is the point ∞, which is difficult to deal with in non-homogeneous form. If, however, we write the quadratic equation in homogeneous form, we obtain $cx_1{}^2 + (d - a)x_1x_2 - bx_2{}^2 = 0$. Then if we let $c = 0$ we still have a quadratic equation one of whose solutions is $x_2 = 0$. This gives the point $(1, 0)$, the point ∞, as an invariant point.

Furthermore, if $c = 0$ and $d = a$, the projectivity of Theorem 5.43 becomes $x' = (ax + b)/a = x + b/a$. The quadratic equation becomes $b = 0$, which is impossible since the given projectivity is not the identity projectivity. The expression $(d - a)^2 + 4bc$ is equal to zero, indicating the existence of two coincident invariant points. However, the homogeneous form of the quadratic equation reduces to $bx_2{}^2 = 0$, giving $x_2 = 0$ as a double root. Hence $(1, 0)$ represents the two coincident invariant points. The point ∞ is therefore an invariant point of the transformation $x' = x + b/a$. This leads to the *definition* $\infty + k = \infty$.

We stop here to summarize the properties defined for the symbol ∞ introduced in Section 3.7:

(1) $k/0 \;=\; \infty$ for $k \neq 0$ (Def. 3.10)
(2) $k \cdot \infty = \infty$ for $k \neq 0$ (Cor. to Th. 5.21)
(3) $k/\infty = 0$ (Cor. 2 to Th. 5.22)
(4) $\infty + k = \infty$ (previous paragraph)

DEFINITION 5.42   A projectivity on a line is called *hyperbolic, parabolic,* or *elliptic* according as it has two, one or no invariant points. Reasons for these names will appear later (Sec. 6.3).

It is of interest to note here that Fig. 3.71 shows a parabolic projectivity on p, with ∞ as invariant point, such that point $n \,\overline{\wedge}\,$ point $(n + 1)$; i.e.,

$$\infty \; 0 \; 1 \; 2 \cdots \overset{B}{\underset{\wedge}{=}} \; \infty \; Q_1 \, Q_2 \, Q_3 \cdots \overset{A}{\underset{\wedge}{=}} \; \infty \; 1 \; 2 \; 3 \cdots \text{giving } \infty \; 0 \; 1 \; 2 \cdots \infty \; \overline{\wedge} \; 1 \; 2 \; 3 \cdots$$

THEOREM 5.44   *If M and N are the two invariant points of a hyperbolic projectivity on a line and if $T(P) = P'$, then $R(M, N, P, P')$ is a constant for the projectivity; i.e., $R(M, N, P, P')$ is independent of P.*

Let $M = (0, 1)$ and $N = (1, 0)$. Then the projectivity has the form

$$\delta x_1' = ax_1, \quad \delta x_2' = dx_2, \quad ad \neq 0 \quad \text{(Cor. 1 to Th. 5.22)}.$$

and

$$R(M, N, P, P') = \frac{\begin{vmatrix} x_1 & x_2 \\ 0 & 1 \end{vmatrix}}{\begin{vmatrix} x_1 & x_2 \\ 1 & 0 \end{vmatrix}} \div \frac{\begin{vmatrix} ax_1 & dx_2 \\ 0 & 1 \end{vmatrix}}{\begin{vmatrix} ax_1 & dx_2 \\ 1 & 0 \end{vmatrix}} = d/a.$$

We now turn to a special type of projectivity on a line.

Definition 5.43 A transformation, other than the identity, whose square is the identity is called an *involution*. Hence if T is an involution, then $T^{-1} = T$ (Th. 4.14).

Theorem 5.45 *Any projective involution on a line has the form* $\delta x_1' = ax_1 + bx_2$, $\delta x_2' = cx_1 - ax_2$, $a^2 + bc \neq 0$, *or, in non-homogeneous form* $x' = (ax + b)/(cx - a)$.

For a projectivity T to be an involution we must have $T^2 = I$; i.e.,

$$\begin{bmatrix} a & b \\ c & d \end{bmatrix}\begin{bmatrix} a & b \\ c & d \end{bmatrix} = \begin{bmatrix} a^2 + bc & ab + bd \\ ac + dc & bc + d^2 \end{bmatrix} = \begin{bmatrix} k & 0 \\ 0 & k \end{bmatrix}.$$

Therefore $ab + bd = 0$, or $b(a + d) = 0$;

$$ac + dc = 0, \quad \text{or} \quad c(a + d) = 0;$$
$$a^2 + bc = bc + d^2, \quad \text{or} \quad a^2 = d^2.$$

From the last of these equations we see that $d = \pm a$. If $d = a \neq 0$, then the first two equations give $b = c = 0$, which makes the transformation itself the identity transformation. Hence $d = -a$ and the theorem is proved.

Corollary *There are no parabolic involutions on a line.*

Theorem 5.46 *If T is a projectivity on a line, and if $T(R) = S$ and $T(S) = R$ for one pair of distinct points R, S, then the transformation is an involution.*

Let r and s be the non-homogeneous coordinates of R and S, respectively. We then have the two equations

$$r = (as + b)/(cs + d),$$
$$s = (ar + b)/(cr + d),$$

or

$$rcs + rd = as + b, \quad rcs + sd = ar + b.$$

From these we have $d(r - s) = a(s - r)$. Hence $d = -a$, since $s \neq r$.

Theorem 5.47 *Any projective involution on a line is determined by two distinct pairs of corresponding points.*

This follows from Theorem 5.46 and the corollary to Theorem 5.24.

THEOREM 5.48   *If A and B are fixed points of an involution T on a line, then C and D are corresponding points if and only if $H(A, B, C, D)$.*

Part I: Given that $A\ B\ C\ D \overline{\wedge} A\ B\ D\ C$. Therefore $R(A, B, C, D) = R(A, B, D, C)$. But if $R(A, B, C, D) = k$, then $R(A, B, D, C) = 1/k$. Then $k = 1/k$, and $k = \pm 1$. But by Theorem 5.35 $k \neq 1$. Therefore $k = -1$ and $H(A, B, C, D)$.

Part II: Given $H(A, B, C, D)$. Hence $R(A, B, C, D) = R(A, B, D, C) = -1$. Therefore $A\ B\ C\ D \overline{\wedge} A\ B\ D\ C$ (Th. 5.37) and the projectivity is an involution (Th. 5.46).

Exercises

1. Prove Theorem 5.41.
2. Prove Theorem 5.42.
3. Find the invariant points of each of the following transformations, assuming that these transformations are projectivities on a line:
   (a) $\delta x_1' = 5x_1 - 6x_2,\ \delta x_2' = x_1$.
   (b) $\delta x_1' = 2x_1 + x_2,\ \delta x_2' = 2x_1 + 3x_2$.
   (c) $\delta x_1' = 2x_1 - x_2,\ \delta x_2' = 2x_1 + 3x_2$.
   (d) $\delta x_1' = 2x_1 - x_2,\ \delta x_2' = 3x_1 - 2x_2$.
   (e) $\delta x_1' = 5x_1,\ \delta x_2' = x_1 + 5x_2$.
   (f) $\delta x_1' = x_1,\ \delta x_2' = x_2$.
4. Prove that $(0, 1)$ is an invariant point of a projectivity on a line if and only if $b = 0$.
5. Prove that $(1, 0)$ is an invariant point of a projectivity on a line if and only if $c = 0$.
6. Prove the corollary to Theorem 5.45.
7. Write out the proof for Theorem 5.47.
8. Find the projective involution that transforms $(1, 0)$ and $(0, 1)$, into $(3, 5)$ and $(7, -3)$ all on the same line.
9. Find the projective involution on a line that transforms $(1, 2)$ and $(1, -1)$ into $(4, -5)$ and $(1, 1)$, respectively.
10. Find the projective involution on a line that has $(1, 1)$ and $(2, 0)$ as invariant points.
11. Find the parabolic projectivity on a line which has $(2, 1)$ as its invariant point and transforms $(2, 3)$ into $(1, 0)$.
12. Show that any projectivity on a line which has 0 and ∞ as invariant points has the form $x' = kx$, and if this is an involution then $k = -1$.
13. In Ex. 3 above, determine which of the transformations are hyperbolic, parabolic, or elliptic. Which are involutions?
14. Show that the set of all hyperbolic transformations of a line onto itself, with the same invariant points forms a group.
15. Let T_1 and T_2 be two projectivities on a line. Discuss the type of projectivity (i.e., hyperbolic, parabolic, elliptic) T_2T_1 may be for all possible classifications of T_1 and T_2.
16. If we add the identity transformation to the set of involutions on a line, does the resulting subset of the projectivities on a line form a subgroup?

17. Does the following set of projectivities on a line form a group? $\delta x_1' = ax_1 + bx_2$, $\delta x_2' = bx_1 + dx_2$, $ad - b^2 \neq 0$.

18. Given the projectivity $x' = (x + 3)/(x - 1)$. Find the invariant points M and N and prove that any other point P and its transform P' are such that $H(M, N, P, P')$.

19. The homogeneous coordinates of four given points in the projective plane are $A(1, 1, 1)$, $B(1, 2, 1)$, $C(3, 1, 2)$, and $D(1, 4, 2)$. Prove that the three pairs of lines AD, BC; DB, AC; CD, AB meet line $x_3 = 0$ in pairs of points in involution.

20. Prove that any projectivity on a line is either an involution or the product of two involutions.

5.5 Collineations in a Plane

The linear transformations or projectivities of the previous sections are one-dimensional; i.e., they deal only with elements in a pencil of points or lines. We shall now consider two-dimensional linear transformations expressed by the following equations where (x_1, x_2, x_3) represents a point in a real projective plane:

$$\delta x_1' = a_{11}x_1 + a_{12}x_2 + a_{13}x_3$$
$$\delta x_2' = a_{21}x_1 + a_{22}x_2 + a_{23}x_3 \qquad a_{ij} \text{ real and}$$
$$\delta x_3' = a_{31}x_1 + a_{32}x_2 + a_{33}x_3 \qquad |a_{ij}| \neq 0.$$

These equations may be written $\delta x_i' = \sum_{j=1}^{3} a_{ij}x_j$, $i = 1, 2, 3$, or, in matrix notation $\delta \mathbf{X}' = \mathbf{AX}$, $|\mathbf{A}| \neq 0$ (cf. Sec. 5.2) where $\mathbf{X}$ and $\mathbf{X}'$ are the column matrices of the homogeneous coordinates of a point and its transform, respectively, and where $\mathbf{A}$ is the matrix of the coefficients a_{ij}. Since $|\mathbf{A}| \neq 0$, the transformation is non-singular, the inverse transformation exists and is given by $\delta \mathbf{X}' = \mathbf{A}^{-1}\mathbf{X}$, or $\delta x_i' = \sum_{j=1}^{3} A_{ji}x_j$, $i = 1, 2, 3$ where A_{ij} is the cofactor of a_{ij} in $|a_{ij}|$.

THEOREM 5.51 *Under a two dimensional linear transformation T, collinear points are transformed into collinear points.*

Let $P(p_1, p_2, p_3)$, $Q(q_1, q_2, q_3)$, and $R(r_1, r_2, r_3)$ be three collinear points and let $T(P) = P'$, $T(Q) = Q'$, and $T(R) = R'$. We wish to show that P', Q', R' are collinear. In matrix notation

$$\delta_1 \mathbf{P}' = \mathbf{AP}, \quad \delta_2 \mathbf{Q}' = \mathbf{AQ}, \quad \delta_3 \mathbf{R}' = \mathbf{AR}.$$

But

$$\mathbf{R} = \lambda_2 \mathbf{P} + \lambda_1 \mathbf{Q} \text{ (Th. 5.12)}.$$

Therefore $\delta_3 \mathbf{R}' = \mathbf{A}(\lambda_2 \mathbf{P} + \lambda_1 \mathbf{Q}) = \lambda_2 \delta_1 \mathbf{P}' + \lambda_1 \delta_2 \mathbf{Q}'$, which makes P', Q', R' collinear (Th. 5.12).

DEFINITION 5.51   A two-dimensional non-singular linear transformation is called a two-dimensional *collineation*.

These collineations may be considered as transformations of the points of one plane onto those of another plane, or as transformations of the set of points of a plane onto itself. In the latter case we speak of *collineations in a plane*.

DEFINITION 5.52   If a point in a plane corresponds to itself under a collineation in the plane, it is called an *invariant point* or *fixed point* of the collineation. If a collineation leaves all points of the plane invariant it is called the *identity collineation*. Such a collineation has the matrix

$$\mathbf{I} = \begin{bmatrix} 1 & 0 & 0 \\ 0 & 1 & 0 \\ 0 & 0 & 1 \end{bmatrix} \quad \text{or} \quad k\mathbf{I} = \begin{bmatrix} k & 0 & 0 \\ 0 & k & 0 \\ 0 & 0 & k \end{bmatrix} \quad k \neq 0.$$

THEOREM 5.52   *The set of collineations in a plane forms a group of transformations.* (Proof left to student).

The collineations as given above are point transformations; i.e., given a point $P(x_1, x_2, x_3)$, direct substitution gives $T(P)$ or $P'(x_1', x_2', x_3')$. We know that under a given collineation the transform of a line is also a line (Th. 5.51). We wish to find the associated line transformation. If we let $\mathbf{U}$ be the row matrix $[u_1\ u_2\ u_3]$ and $\mathbf{U}'$ be the row matrix $[u_1'\ u_2'\ u_3']$ then $\mathbf{UX} = \mathbf{0}$ represents the equation of the given line and $\mathbf{U'X'} = \mathbf{0}$ represents the equation of its transform. We wish to find $\mathbf{U}'$ when $\mathbf{U}$ is given. From the collineation $\delta\mathbf{X}' = \mathbf{AX}$, we have

$$\delta\mathbf{U'X'} = \mathbf{U'AX}$$

so that line $\mathbf{U'X'} = \mathbf{0}$ is the transform of line $\mathbf{U'AX} = \mathbf{0}$. But $\mathbf{U'X'} = \mathbf{0}$ is the transform of line $\mathbf{UX} = \mathbf{0}$. Therefore, $\mathbf{U} = k\mathbf{U'A}$ and hence $k\mathbf{U} = \mathbf{UA}^{-1}$. We have then the following:

THEOREM 5.53   *The line transformation associated with the point transformation* $\delta\mathbf{X}' = \mathbf{AX}$ *is* $k\mathbf{U}' = \mathbf{UA}^{-1}$, *which may be written as* $ku_i' =$
$$\sum_{j=1}^{3} A_{ij}u_j, \quad i = 1, 2, 3.$$

The point transformation and its associated line transformation represent the *same* collineation.

COROLLARY   *Under a collineation, concurrent lines correspond to concurrent lines.*

THEOREM 5.54 *For a given choice of reference triangle and unit point in a plane there exists a unique non-singular collineation that transforms any four points in the plane, no three of which are collinear, into any four points in the plane, no three of which are collinear.*

The proof is analogous to that of Theorem 5.23. The dual is proven in a similar manner using the equations of Theorem 5.53.

COROLLARY *A collineation in the plane with four invariant points, no three of which are collinear, is the identity collineation in the plane.*

THEOREM 5.55 *Any collineation in a plane establishes a projectivity between the elements of two corresponding pencils.*

Let P, Q, R be three points of a pencil of points and let $T(P) = P'$, $T(Q) = Q'$, $T(R) = R'$. P, Q, R are collinear and hence so are P', Q', R' (Th. 5.51). As in the proof of Theorem 5.51 we have $\mathbf{R} = \lambda_2\mathbf{P} + \lambda_1\mathbf{Q}$ and $\delta_3\mathbf{R}' = \lambda_2\delta_1\mathbf{P}' + \lambda_1\delta_2\mathbf{Q}'$ or $\mathbf{R}' = \mu_2\mathbf{P}' + \mu_1\mathbf{Q}'$, where $\delta_3\mu_1 = \delta_2\lambda_1$ and $\delta_3\mu_2 = \delta_1\lambda_2$. Hence $\mu = k\lambda$, which is a projectivity.

COROLLARY *The cross-ratio of four elements in a pencil is an invariant of the group of collineations.*

Note that since collinearity, concurrence, and cross-ratio are invariant under collineations, then Theorem 5.54 enables us to simplify analytic proofs involving these properties by choosing any four points, no three of which are collinear, as the vertices of the reference triangle and the unit point. Thus Axiom 6 ("The diagonal points of a complete quadrangle are not collinear") may be verified by using the vertices of the triangle of reference and the unit point as vertices of the quadrangle, and finding the equations of appropriate lines and their points of intersection.

The corollary to Theorem 5.54 tells us that a collineation other than the identity cannot have four invariant points, no three of which are collinear. It would seem then that the analog of Theorem 5.43 would allow three non-collinear, two, one, or no invariant points in the plane. We find however, in the case of the real projective plane, that the following theorem holds.

THEOREM 5.56 *Under any collineation in the real projective plane, there is at least one invariant point and at least one invariant line.*

For invariant points, we seek solutions for x_1, x_2, x_3, not all zero, and $\delta \neq 0$, satisfying the three equations represented by $\delta X = AX$, $|A| \neq 0$. These are equivalent to

$$(a_{11} - \delta)x_1 + \quad a_{12}x_2 + \quad a_{13}x_3 = 0$$
$$a_{21}x_1 + (a_{22} - \delta)x_2 + \quad a_{23}x_3 = 0$$
$$a_{31}x_1 + \quad a_{32}x_2 + (a_{33} - \delta)x_3 = 0.$$

For a solution of the required type to exist, the determinant of the coefficients must be zero; i.e., $|A - \delta I| = 0$. This determinant is a polynomial in δ, called the *characteristic polynomial* of the matrix A. Its roots are called the *characteristic values* of A. Since this is a cubic polynomial with real coefficients it has at least one real root. Since $|A| \neq 0$, the root $\delta \neq 0$. Hence we have at least one invariant point.

By applying a similar argument to the equations of Theorem 5.53 we obtain at least one invariant line. This line is not necessarily pointwise invariant. To see the relationship between the invariant points and the invariant lines, consider the matrix equation $kU = UA^{-1}$ for the invariant lines. This is equivalent to $kUA = U$ or $UA = (1/k)U$ or

$$U[A - (1/k)I] = 0.$$

Therefore for a solution of the required type to exist, k must satisfy the equation $|A - (1/k)I| = 0$. Hence $k = 1/\delta$ and there are as many invariant lines as there are invariant points. The characteristic values of the matrix A may be used to determine the invariant lines as well as the invariant points.

For a collineation other than the identity, a given value of δ may yield one invariant point or a whole line of invariant points, as is illustrated in the following: Let a collineation be given by the equations

$$\delta x_1' = 2x_1 + x_3$$
$$\delta x_2' = 2x_2 + 3x_3$$
$$\delta x_3' = x_3.$$

The characteristic polynomial is

$$\begin{vmatrix} 2 - \delta & 0 & 1 \\ 0 & 2 - \delta & 3 \\ 0 & 0 & 1 - \delta \end{vmatrix}$$

whose roots are $\delta = 1$, and $\delta = 2$. For $\delta = 1$ the equations for the invariant points become

$$x_1 + x_3 = 0$$
$$x_2 + 3x_3 = 0.$$

These yield the invariant point $(1, 3, -1)$. For $\delta = 2$ the equations all reduce to $x_3 = 0$. Thus any point of the form $(x_1, x_2, 0)$ is an invariant point giving a whole line of invariant points.

DEFINITION 5.53 A collineation with one invariant point P and one line p of invariant points, where P is not on p, is called a *homology*. P is called the *center* and p the *axis* of the homology. The illustration above is a homology.

Under a homology, every line m through the invariant point P is an invariant line since m has two invariant points, namely P and $m \cdot p$. Therefore a homology induces a hyperbolic projectivity on every line through its center. With the help of Theorem 5.44 we may then prove the following:

THEOREM 5.57 *Under a given homology T with center P and axis p, any point X not on p has a transform $X' = T(X)$ such that (1) P, X, X' are collinear and (2) if $p \cdot PX = Q$, then $R(P, Q, X, X')$ is constant for all X.*

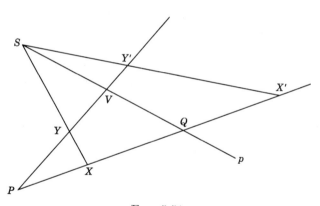

FIG. 5.51

Part (1) is simply a restatement of the previous paragraph. For (2) Theorem 5.44 gives $R(P, Q, X, X')$ a constant for all X on the same line. Therefore, it remains to show that if Y is a point not collinear with P and X, and if $T(Y) = Y'$ then $R(P, Q, X, X') = R(P, V, Y, Y')$ where $V = PY \cdot p$ (Fig. 5.51). Let $S = XY \cdot p$. Since $T(S) = S$ and $T(X) = X'$, then $T(\text{line } SX)$ $= \text{line } SX'$. Also, since line PY is a fixed line, $T(SX \cdot PY) = T(SX' \cdot PY)$; i. e., $T(Y) = SX' \cdot PY = Y'$. But $P \; Q \; X \; X' \overset{S}{\underset{\wedge}{=}} P \; V \; Y \; Y'$ and therefore $R(P, Q, X, X') = R(P, V, Y, Y')$.

DEFINITION 5.54   If under a homology, the constant cross-ratio of Theorem 5.57 is -1, the transformation is called a *harmonic homology*.

A full discussion of the types of characteristic values of a matrix and the corresponding sets of invariant points and lines appears in Levy, Chapter III, Section 11. We shall discuss some of these in Chapter 6 in connection with subgeometries of projective geometry.

Exercises

1. Prove Theorem 5.52.

2. Given the matrix $\begin{bmatrix} 2 & 0 & 1 \\ 0 & 2 & 3 \\ 0 & 0 & 1 \end{bmatrix}$

(a) Write out the corresponding point transformation T and find $T(1, 2, 3)$.
(b) Write out the associated line transformation and find the line corresponding to line $[1, 2, 3]$.

3. Prove Theorem 5.54 and its corollary.

4. Verify Axiom 6 as suggested in this section.

5. Find the collineation that transforms the points $A(1, 0, 1)$, $B(2, 0, 1)$, $C(0, 1, 1)$, $D(0, 2, 1)$ into X, Y, Z, U, respectively.

6. (a) Find the inverse of the collineation in Ex. 5. (b) Find the transform of line $x_1 + x_2 + x_3 = 0$ under the collineation in Ex. 5.

7. Find the collineation which transforms the points $(2, 1, 0)$, $(-1, 1, 2)$, $(0, 1, 1)$ into X, Y, Z, respectively, and leaves U invariant.

8. Show that a collineation which has the vertices of the reference triangle as invariant points has a diagonal matrix.

9. Find the invariant points and lines of the following:
(a) $\delta x_1' = a x_1 + x_2,\ \delta x_2' = a x_2,\ \delta x_3' = b x_3,\ a \neq b,\ ab \neq 0$.
(b) $\delta x_1' = x_1,\ \delta x_2' = x_2 + x_3,\ \delta x_3' = x_3$.
(c) $\delta x_1' = a x_1 + x_2,\ \delta x_2' = a x_2 + x_3,\ \delta x_3' = a x_3,\ a \neq 0$.

10. Show that the following collineation is a homology

$$\delta x_1' = x_1, \quad \delta x_2' = x_2, \quad \delta x_3' = 2 x_1 - x_3.$$

11. Show that if a collineation T has only one invariant point A and if $B \neq A$, then $T(B)$ is distinct from both A and B.

5.6   Correlations, Polarities, and Conics

If in the equations for a collineation we replace the x_i' by u_i, we obtain a transformation that transforms points into lines, and lines into points; i.e., the elements of the plane are transformed into their dual elements. Such a transformation is called a correlation. To be more precise we give the following definition.

DEFINITION 5.61   A non-singular *correlation* in a projective plane is a one-to-one correspondence between points (x_1, x_2, x_3) and lines $[u_1, u_2, u_3]$ expressed by the equations represented by $\delta \mathbf{U}^t = \mathbf{A} \mathbf{X}$, $|\mathbf{A}| \neq 0$, where the matrices $\mathbf{A}$, $\mathbf{X}$, $\mathbf{U}$ have the definitions given in Section 5.5, and the superscript t indicates the transpose matrix. These equations may also be written as

$$(1) \quad \delta u_i = \sum_{j=1}^{3} a_{ij} x_j, \quad i = 1, 2, 3.$$

Solving for the x_i in terms of the u_i gives $\mathbf{X} = \delta \mathbf{A}^{-1} \mathbf{U}^t$ or

$$(2) \quad \delta' x_i = \sum_{j=1}^{3} A_{ji} u_j, \quad i = 1, 2, 3$$

for the inverse correlation.

As in the previous section we see that a correlation transforms collinear points into concurrent lines and thus induces a transformation of lines into points given by $k\mathbf{X}^t = \mathbf{U}\mathbf{A}^{-1}$ or by

$$(3) \quad kx_i = \sum_{j=1}^{3} A_{ij} u_j, \quad i = 1, 2, 3.$$

The inverse of this is $k'\mathbf{U} = \mathbf{X}^t\mathbf{A}$ or

$$(4) \quad k'u_i = \sum_{j=1}^{3} a_{ji} x_j, \quad i = 1, 2, 3.$$

Equations (1) and (3) represent the same correlation, while (2) and (4) represent the inverse correlation.

Now if a point P corresponds under equation (1) to a line p, then of course p corresponds under the inverse transformation (2) to point P. But line p would not necessarily correspond to point P under the induced transformation (3). However, if a correlation is such that if a point P corresponds to a line p under equations (1) then p corresponds to P under equations (3) for all points P, then the correlation is involutory and is the same as its inverse. In this case the equations (1), (2), (3), and (4) must all represent the same correlation. This will happen if and only if $a_{ij} = a_{ji}$; i.e., if the matrix of the correlation is symmetric.

DEFINITION 5.62   A correlation whose matrix is symmetric is called a *polarity*. Under a polarity if a point P corresponds to a line p, then p corresponds to P. The line p is called the *polar* of its corresponding point P, and the point P is called the *pole* of the line p.

THEOREM 5.61   *Polars of distinct points are distinct lines.* (This is an immediate consequence of the definitions.)

THEOREM 5.62   *A point P is on the polar of point Q if and only if Q is on the polar of P.*

Under the polarity $\delta \mathbf{U}^t = \mathbf{AX}$, the polar p of point P is given by $\delta \mathbf{U}_p{}^t = \mathbf{AP}$. Its equation is $\mathbf{U}_p \mathbf{X} = 0$ or $\mathbf{P}^t \mathbf{AX} = 0$. For Q to be on this line, we have $\mathbf{P}^t \mathbf{AQ} = 0$. Therefore the transpose $\mathbf{Q}^t \mathbf{A}^t \mathbf{P} = 0$. But for a polarity $\mathbf{A}^t = \mathbf{A}$. Therefore $\mathbf{Q}^t \mathbf{A} \, \mathbf{P} = 0$ which is the condition that P be on the polar of Q.

DEFINITION 5.63   Two points are called *conjugate points* if each is on the polar of the other. A point which is on its own polar is called a *self-conjugate point*.

The student is reminded to write out the duals of all definitions and theorems.

THEOREM 5.63   *The set of self-conjugate points of a polarity is the set of points satisfying the equation*

$$a_{11}x_1{}^2 + 2a_{12}x_1x_2 + a_{22}x_2{}^2 + 2a_{13}x_1x_3 + 2a_{23}x_2x_3 + a_{33}x_3{}^2 = 0.$$

In the proof of Theorem 5.62 we saw that the polar of point P has the equation $\mathbf{P}^t \mathbf{A} \, \mathbf{X} = 0$. For P to be on this, $\mathbf{P}^t \mathbf{AP} = 0$. Hence the locus of all such points has the matrix equation $\mathbf{X}^t \mathbf{AX} = 0$, which expands into the required equation.

DEFINITION 5.64   The set of self-conjugate points of a polarity is called a *point conic;* the set of self-conjugate lines is called a *line conic* (Von Staudt, 1847).

In matrix form a point conic has the equation $\mathbf{X}^t \mathbf{A} \, \mathbf{X} = 0$, where $\mathbf{A}$ is a symmetric matrix and $|\mathbf{A}| \neq 0$. (We are interested here only in non-singular conics. For a discussion of other conics see the references at the end of this chapter). $\mathbf{A}$ is called the matrix of both the polarity and the conic. Thus a polarity determines a conic. Conversely, a homogeneous quadratic equation in x_1, x_2, x_3 can be put into the form $\mathbf{X}^t \mathbf{A} \, \mathbf{X} = 0$ where $\mathbf{A}$ is symmetric and, if $|\mathbf{A}| \neq 0$, this determines a non-singular polarity.

DEFINITION 5.65   A line p is the *polar of a point P with respect to a given conic* if p corresponds to P under the polarity determined by the conic. A point P is the *pole of a line p with respect to a given conic* if P corresponds to p under the polarity determined by the conic.

We interrupt our discussion to reconcile Von Staudt's definition of a point conic given above with Steiner's given in Definition 3.91. We shall show that the latter leads to the same equation as that given in Theorem 5.63.

Let $m = m_1x_1 + m_2x_2 + m_3x_3$, and $n = n_1x_1 + n_2x_2 + n_3x_3$ and let $m = 0$ and $n = 0$ be two distinct lines in the plane. Then any line in the pencil having these as base lines is of the form $\lambda_2 m + \lambda_1 n = 0$. Let a conic be generated by two projective pencils $\lambda_2 m + \lambda_1 n = 0$ and $\mu_2 p + \mu_1 q = 0$ where the projectivity is given by $\mu = k\lambda$. Then the conic is the set of points of intersection of $\lambda_2 m + \lambda_1 n = 0$ and $\lambda_2 p + k\lambda_1 q = 0$. Eliminating λ_1/λ_2 from these two equations gives the conic as $np - kmq = 0$; i.e.,

$$(n_1x_1 + n_2x_2 + n_3x_3)(p_1x_1 + p_2x_2 + p_3x_3)$$
$$-k(m_1x_1 + m_2x_2 + m_3x_3)(q_1x_1 + q_2x_2 + q_3x_3) = 0.$$

This is a homogeneous equation of the second degree of the form

$$a_{11}x_1^2 + 2a_{12}x_1x_2 + a_{22}x_2^2 + 2a_{13}x_1x_3 + 2a_{23}x_2x_3 + a_{33}x_3^2 = 0.$$

We now resume our discussion of polarities, poles, and polars.

Theorem 5.64 *If P is on the point conic determined by a given polarity, its polar p has no other point on the conic.*

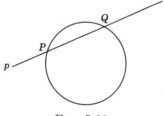

Fig. 5.61

Since P is on the conic it is on its own polar p. If another point Q on the conic is also on p (Fig. 5.61) then line PQ is p. But since Q is on the polar of P, P must be on the polar of Q; and since Q is on the conic it is on its own polar. Hence PQ is also the polar of Q, contradicting Theorem 5.61.

Definition 5.66 The polar of a point on the point conic is called the *tangent* to the conic at the given point.

Theorem 5.65 *The tangents to a point conic are the lines of the corresponding line conic.*

Let the point conic be $\mathbf{X}^t\mathbf{A}\mathbf{X} = \mathbf{0}$, where $\mathbf{A}$ is symmetric, and hence the corresponding line conic is $\mathbf{U}\mathbf{A}^{-1}\mathbf{U}^t = \mathbf{0}$. Then the tangent at the point (x_1, x_2, x_3) is given by $\mathbf{U}^t = \mathbf{A}\mathbf{X}$. But this satisfies the equation of the line conic since $\mathbf{U}\mathbf{A}^{-1}\mathbf{U}^t = \mathbf{X}^t\mathbf{A}^t\mathbf{A}^{-1}\mathbf{A}\mathbf{X} = \mathbf{X}^t\mathbf{A}\mathbf{X} = \mathbf{0}$.

THEOREM 5.66   *The point of intersection of two tangents to a point conic is the pole of line joining the points of tangency.*

This follows from Definition 5.66 and Theorem 5.62.

DEFINITION 5.67   If in the real projective plane, the polar of P with respect to a given conic does not intersect the conic, the point P is said to be an *interior point* of the conic. If the polar of P intersects the conic in two distinct points then P is said to be an *exterior point*.

It can be shown that if a line intersects a conic in two distinct points, two line segments are determined (Th. 5.38), one of which consists entirely of interior points and the other of exterior points.

DEFINITION 5.68   If with respect to a given conic there exists a triangle such that each vertex is the pole of opposite side, the triangle is called a *self-polar triangle*.

THEOREM 5.67   *If a complete quadrangle is inscribed in a conic, its diagonal triangle is a self-polar triangle.*

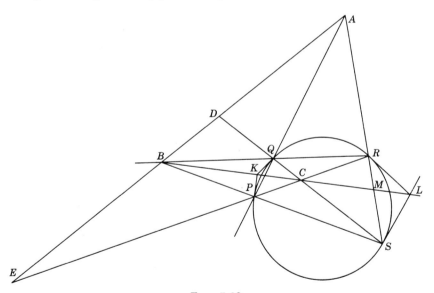

FIG. 5.62

Let $PQRS$ be the complete quadrangle (Fig. 5.62) with diagonal triangle ABC. Let the tangents at Q and P intersect in K, and the tangents at R and S intersect in L. Then Corollary 2 of Theorem 3.93 shows that B, K, C, L

are collinear. But A is on the polar of K and also on the polar of L (Th. 5.66). Therefore KL, or BC, is the polar of A. Similarly, AC is the polar of B and AB is the polar of C.

To construct the polar of any point on the plane, but not on the conic, we draw any two lines through the given point which intersect the conic in four distinct points. These four points determine a complete quadrangle of which the given point is a diagonal point. The other two diagonal points determine the required polar. To construct the polar of a point on the conic (i.e., to construct a tangent to a conic at a given point on it) we use Corollary 1 of Theorem 3.93 on the pentagon formed by the given point and four other points.

COROLLARY (to Th. 5.67) *A line m through a point A not on the conic, intersects the conic in points which are harmonic conjugates with respect to A and the point of intersection of m with the polar of A.*

Let m be line ARS of Fig. 5.62; let $M = m \cdot BC$, $D = AB \cdot QS$, $E = AB \cdot PR$. By Definition 3.42, we have $H(A, B, E, D)$. But $A\ B\ E\ D \stackrel{C}{\wedge} A\ M\ R\ S$. Hence $H(A, M, R, S)$. The polar of a point A with respect to a given conic is often defined as the locus of the harmonic conjugates of A with respect to the points of intersection of the conic with lines through A.

THEOREM 5.68 *Under a collineation a conic is transformed into a conic.*

Given the conic $\mathbf{X'AX} = \mathbf{0}$, $\mathbf{A}$ symmetric and non-singular, and the collineation $\delta\mathbf{X'} = \mathbf{BX}$, $|\mathbf{B}| \neq 0$, we seek the transform of the conic under the collineation. From the equation of the collineation we have $\mathbf{X} = \delta\mathbf{B^{-1}X'}$, and therefore $\mathbf{X'} = \delta\mathbf{X'^t(B^{-1})^t}$. Thus the conic $\mathbf{X'AX} = \mathbf{0}$ becomes

$$\delta^2\mathbf{X'^t(B^{-1})^tAB^{-1}X'} = \mathbf{0}.$$

This is equivalent to $\mathbf{X'^tCX'} = \mathbf{0}$, where $\mathbf{C} = \mathbf{(B^{-1})^tAB^{-1}}$, which is a non-singular symmetric matrix. Therefore, under a collineation the transform of a conic is a conic.

As a result of Theorems 5.68 and 5.54 we may choose any four points, no three of which are collinear, as the triangle of reference and unit point, and reduce the equation of a given conic to a simpler form. This is done in the following theorems.

THEOREM 5.69 *If the reference triangle is a self-polar triangle with respect to a conic, the conic has a diagonal matrix; i.e., the equation of the conic has the form*

$$a_{11}x_1^2 + a_{22}x_2^2 + a_{33}x_3^2 = 0.$$

If XYZ is a self-polar triangle, then $X(1, 0, 0)$ is the pole of $YZ[1, 0, 0]$, $Y(0, 1, 0)$ is the pole of $XZ[0, 1, 0]$ and $Z(0, 0, 1)$ is the pole of $XY[0, 0, 1]$. Substituting these values in the equations of the general polarity we find that $a_{ij} = 0$ when $i \neq j$. Therefore the matrix is a diagonal matrix.

Thus any conic may be expressed in the above form. If all the a_{ii} have the same sign we can assume that they are all positive. Then the collineation $\delta x_i' = (a_{ii})^{1/2}x_i$, $i = 1$, 2, 3, reduces the equation of the conic to $x_1^2 + x_2^2 + x_3^2 = 0$, which is an imaginary conic; i.e., it has no points in the real projective plane. For the conic to be real, one of the a_{ii}, say a_{33}, must be negative. Then the collineation $\delta x_i' = (|a_{ii}|)^{1/2}x_i$ reduces the equation to $x_1^2 + x_2^2 - x_3^2 = 0$. Thus

COROLLARY   *Any non-singular conic can be expressed in one of the forms:* $x_1^2 + x_2^2 + x_3^2 = 0$, *or* $x_1^2 + x_2^2 - x_3^2 = 0$.

DEFINITION 5.69   A non-singular polarity whose associated conic is real is called a *hyperbolic polarity;* one whose associated conic is imaginary is called an *elliptic polarity.*

The relationship of these polarities to the hyperbolic and elliptic geometries will be discussed in Chapter 7.

Exercises

1. Given the polarity: $\delta u_1 = 2x_1 - x_3$, $\delta u_2 = x_2 + x_3$, $\delta u_3 = -x_1 + x_2$, find (a) the equations of the associated point conic and line conic, (b) the pole of the line $[1, 1, 1]$ and (c) a point conjugate to the point $(1, 1, 1)$.

2. Given the conic $x_1^2 + 2x_2^2 + 5x_3^2 - 2x_2x_3 - 2x_1x_3 - 4x_1x_2 = 0$, find (a) the tangent at point $(1, 1, 1)$, (b) the polar of $(3, 1, 5)$, (c) the tangents from the point $(1, -2, 0)$.

3. Find the polar of point $(1, 0, 2)$ with respect to the line conic $u_1^2 + 2u_1u_2 - 2u_2u_3 + u_3^2 = 0$.

4. Given conic $3x_1^2 + 3x_2^2 + 3x_3^2 + 15x_1x_2 + 10x_1x_3 + 5x_2x_3 = 0$. (a) Prove that the polars of $(1, 0, 0)$, $(0, 1, 0)$, $(0, 0, 1)$ meet lines $x_1 = 0$, $x_2 = 0$, $x_3 = 0$, respectively, in three collinear points. (b) Find the points of intersection of the conic with line $x_2 = 0$.

5. Prove Theorem 5.66.

6. State and illustrate the duals of Theorem 5.67 and corollary.

7. Prove that a correlation that makes each vertex of the reference triangle correspond to its opposite side is a polarity.

8. Find the point which is conjugate to the point $(1, 2, 3)$ with respect to the conic $x_1^2 + 2x_2^2 + 3x_3^2 = 0$, and which lies on the line $x_1 + 2x_2 + 3x_3 = 0$.

9. Prove that the polar of the point $(1, 2, 3)$ with respect to all conics of the form $a_{23}x_2x_3 + a_{13}x_1x_3 + a_{12}x_1x_2 = 0$, where $a_{12} + a_{13} + a_{23} = 0$, passes through the point $(1, 1, 0)$.

10. Prove that the polars of collinear points are concurrent and dually.

11. Show that if the vertices of the reference triangle lie on a conic, the equation of the conic has the form $a_{12}x_1x_2 + a_{23}x_2x_3 + a_{13}x_1x_3 = 0$.

12. If A and B are two distinct conjugate points with respect to a conic and if C and D are two points on the conic collinear with B and if AC and AD meet the conic in E and F, respectively, show that E, F, B are collinear.

13. If A and B are two distinct points not on a given conic, whose polars are a and b, respectively, and if $P = AB \cdot a$ and $Q = a \cdot b$, show that P and Q are conjugate points.

14. Show that the triangle with vertices $(1, 0, 1)$, $(1, 1, 0)$, $(0, 1, 1)$ is self-polar with respect to the conic

$$x_1{}^2 - 6x_1x_2 + x_2{}^2 + 2x_1x_3 + 2x_2x_3 + x_3{}^2 = 0.$$

15. If A, B, C are three distinct points on a conic, prove that lines AB and AC are harmonic conjugates with respect to the tangent at A and the line joining A to the pole of BC.

16. Show that a harmonic homology whose center and axis are pole and polar with respect to a conic, keeps that conic invariant.

17. Prove that the set of collineations that leaves a given conic invariant, forms a subgroup of the group of collineations.

18. Prove that the pole–polar relationship is invariant under a collineation.

19. Show that a triangle ABC inscribed in a conic and the circumscribed triangle DEF whose sides are tangent to the conic at points A, B, C, are perspective from a point.

20. Show that the lines joining the vertices of any triangle to the poles of the opposite sides, with respect to a given conic, are concurrent.

21. Write out the duals of all definitions and theorems of this section.

5.7 The Projective Group

The correlations of the previous section transform points into lines and lines into points. If a point and a line are incident, then under a correlation the corresponding line and point are also incident. Collinear points are transformed into concurrent lines and conversely, preserving cross-ratio. A complete quadrangle is transformed into a complete quadrilateral. In short, any figure is transformed into its dual.

The set of correlations does not, however, form a group since the product of two correlations is a collineation. Thus the *general projective group* in a plane is taken to consist of the set of non-singular correlations and non-singular collineations in the plane. The presence of correlations in this group gives analytic expression to the principle of duality.

For our purposes, however, we shall consider only the point-to-point transformations (and the induced line-to-line transformations) given by the group of non-singular collineations in the plane. Using Klein's concept of geometry (Sec. 4.3) we shall define *real projective geometry* of the plane as the study of properties invariant under this group and call such properties *projective properties*. These include the incidence relations and hence collinearity of points and concurrence of lines; the cross-ratio of four elements and hence the separation and the harmonic relations; the property of a subset of points or lines being a conic and the pole–polar relationship.

However, we cannot distinguish one type of conic from another nor one type of quadrangle from another. The corollary to Theorem 5.69 makes all real conics projectively equivalent; while Theorem 5.54 makes all quadjectively equivalent. In the next chapter we shall consider subgroups of the projective group which lead to geometries in which these distinctions can be made and which lead eventually to Euclidean geometry.

References

Adler, Chap. 10; Fishback, Chaps. 8, 9; Levy, Chaps. II–IV; Meserve, Chap. 4; Woods, Chap. VI; Young (2), Chap. VIII.

CHAPTER 6

SUBGEOMETRIES OF PROJECTIVE GEOMETRY

In this chapter we consider subgroups of the projective group of collineations. We show how to get from the general projective collineations to the rigid motions of the Euclidean plane, obtaining different geometries by changing the transformation group. Thus Euclidean geometry is placed in its proper perspective as but one type of geometry in a much larger set of geometries.

6.1 Affine Transformations

A collineation in the real projective plane that leaves a given line invariant is called *an affine transformation*. The set of affine transformations forms a group called the *affine group* which is a subgroup of the projective group. The corresponding geometry, the study of properties left invariant under the affine group of transformations, is called *affine geometry*, a subgeometry of projective geometry. We shall call the invariant line the *ideal line* and denote it by l_∞. All other lines in the real projective plane are *ordinary lines*. Note that *any* line in the projective plane may be chosen as l_∞. The points on l_∞ are *ideal points;* all other points in the projective plane are *ordinary points*. An affine transformation transforms ordinary points into ordinary points and ideal points into ideal points. From now on we shall assume that the words "point" and "line" refer to *ordinary* points and lines unless otherwise specified. The *affine plane* is the projective plane with l_∞ omitted. An affine line is an ordinary line with its ideal point omitted. We note that in the affine plane the principle of duality does not hold since two affine lines do not always determine a point. In what follows we shall assume that the affine plane is embedded in the projective plane and shall use projective theorems to help prove affine theorems. Thus when we speak of the ideal point of a given line, we shall mean the point of intersection of l_∞ with the projective line on which the given affine line lies.

To get an analytic form for affine transformations, we shall assume that the coordinate system has been so chosen that l_∞ has the equation $x_3 = 0$. Then all points in the affine plane will have non-homogeneous coordinates

(x, y) as well as homogeneous coordinates (x_1, x_2, x_3), $x_3 \neq 0$, and we shall feel free to use whichever are more convenient at any particular time. We now seek an analytic expression for those collineations which leave $x_3 = 0$ invariant.

We start with the general collineation

$$\delta x_1' = a_{11}x_1 + a_{12}x_2 + a_{13}x_3$$
$$\delta x_2' = a_{21}x_1 + a_{22}x_2 + a_{23}x_3 \qquad |a_{ij}| \neq 0.$$
$$\delta x_3' = a_{31}x_1 + a_{32}x_2 + a_{33}x_3$$

For $x_3 = 0$ to imply $x_3' = 0$, it is necessary and sufficient that $a_{31} = a_{32} = 0$. Then since $|a_{ij}| \neq 0$, we have $a_{33} \neq 0$ and the coefficients can be chosen so that $a_{33} = 1$. Therefore any affine transformation has the form

$$\delta x_1' = a_{11}x_1 + a_{12}x_2 + a_{13}x_3$$
$$\delta x_2' = a_{21}x_1 + a_{22}x_2 + a_{23}x_3 \qquad |a_{ij}| \neq 0.$$
$$\delta x_3' = \qquad\qquad\qquad\qquad x_3$$

In non-homogeneous coordinates this becomes

$$x' = ax + by + c$$
$$y' = dx + ey + f \qquad (ae - bd) \neq 0.$$

THEOREM 6.11   *The set of affine transformations forms a group.* (Proof left to student.)

THEOREM 6.12   *There is a unique affine transformation under which the vertices A, B, C of any triangle correspond to the vertices A', B', C' of any other triangle.*

This is proven by using the dual of Theorem 5.54 which gives a unique collineation under which the lines AB, BC, AC, and l_∞ correspond to the lines $A'B'$, $B'C'$, $A'C'$, and l_∞, respectively. Then since l_∞ corresponds to itself, this collineation is an affine transformation. Thus any two triangles are "equivalent" under affine transformations.

THEOREM 6.13   *A line has the equation* $ax_1 + bx_2 + cx_3 = 0$ *if and only if its ideal point is* $(b, -a, 0)$. (Proof left to student.)

Exercises

1. Prove Theorem 6.11. Is this group commutative?

2. Prove Theorem 6.13.

3. Prove that the Euclidean distance $[(x_2 - x_1)^2 + (y_2 - y_1)^2]^{1/2}$ is not invariant under the general affine transformation. Under what conditions on the coefficients of the transformation would the Euclidean distance be invariant?

4. Find the affine transformation that transforms $A(0, 0)$, $B(1, 0)$, $C(0, 1)$, into $A'(0, 0)$, $B'(5, 1)$, $C'(2, -3)$, respectively.

6.2   Parallelism and Congruence in the Affine Plane

DEFINITION 6.21   Two ordinary lines that intersect in an ideal point are said to be *parallel*. Therefore two lines are parallel if they have no point of intersection in the affine plane.

From Theorem 6.13 we see that two distinct parallel lines have homogeneous equations of the form

$$ax_1 + bx_2 + cx_3 = 0$$
$$ax_1 + bx_2 + dx_3 = 0 \qquad c \neq d.$$

In non-homogeneous form these become

$$ax + by + c = 0$$
$$ax + by + d = 0 \qquad c \neq d.$$

the familiar Euclidean form for parallel lines.

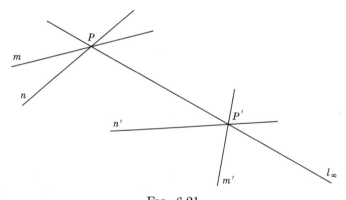

FIG. 6.21

THEOREM 6.21   *Under affine transformations, parallel lines correspond to parallel lines; i.e., parallelism is an affine invariant.*

In Fig. 6.21, m and n are the given parallel lines meeting at P on l_∞. Under an affine transformation T, $T(P) = P'$ also on l_∞. But $P' = m' \cdot n'$ where $m' = T(m)$, and $n' = T(n)$. Hence m' and n' are also parallel by definition.

Here the student should note that, since l_∞ is *any* given line in the projective plane, parallel lines may not "look" parallel. Again the student is cautioned against using "intuition" and is asked to remember that figures have only the properties given to them by axioms, definitions, and theorems. He should then have no difficulty proving the next three theorems.

THEOREM 6.22   *Through a given point not on a given line, there exists just one line parallel to the given line.*

THEOREM 6.23   *Two distinct lines parallel to the same line are parallel to each other.*

THEOREM 6.24   *If a line intersects one of two parallel lines, it intersects the other.*

DEFINITION 6.22   A *parallelogram* is a complete quadrilateral with two opposite vertices on the ideal line. The *diagonals* of the parallelogram lie on the lines joining the remaining two pairs of opposite vertices, which are called *the vertices* of the parallelogram.

DEFINITION 6.23   If A, B, C are three distinct points on a line whose ideal point is P, then C is *between* A and B if and only if $AB \ // \ CP$.

DEFINITION 6.24   By *segment AB* we shall mean the set of points A, B and all points X such that X is between A and B. [See Fig. 6.22(a) and 6.22(b) where segment AB is the heavy portion of the line. In both cases the segment AB is closed. Recall Sec. 3.6.]

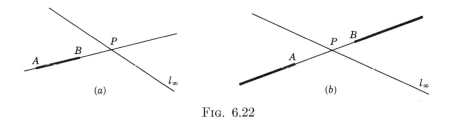

FIG. 6.22

Though the Euclidean distance function is not an affine invariant (Ex. 3 of Sec. 6.1), it is possible to introduce a limited form of congruence that is preserved by affine transformations.

DEFINITION 6.25   Two line segments AB and CD are said to be *congruent* if AB and CD are opposite sides of a parallelogram [Fig. 6.23(a)], or if there is a pair of points M, N such that $ABMN$ and $CDMN$ are parallelograms [Fig. 6.23(b)]. Due to Theorem 6.21, congruence, as thus defined, is an affine invariant.

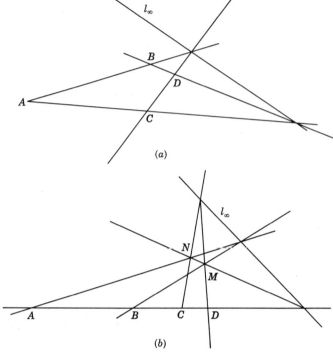

FIG. 6.23

DEFINITION 6.26 M is the *midpoint* of segment AB if it is the harmonic conjugate, with respect to A and B, of the ideal point P of the line AB; i.e., if $H(A, B, P, M)$.

Note that the above definition does not say that the midpoint divides a segment into two congruent segments. This must be proven on the basis of Definition 6.25 (see Cor. to Th. 6.26).

The following theorem is an immediate consequence of the definitions involved and of the invariance of the harmonic relation under any collineation.

THEOREM 6.25   *Under an affine transformation the transform of the midpoint of a segment is the midpoint of the transform of the segment; i.e., if $T(AB) = A'B'$ under an affine transformation T, and if M is the midpoint of AB, then $T(M) = M'$ such that M' is the midpoint of $A'B'$. Thus we say that midpoint is an affine invariant.*

THEOREM 6.26   *A line joining the midpoints of two sides of a triangle is parallel to the third side.*

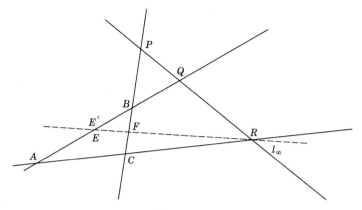

Fig. 6.24

In Fig. 6.24 E and F are midpoints of sides AB and BC, and P, Q, R are the ideal points of the lines CB, AB, AC, respectively. We wish to show that $EF \parallel AC$. Let E' be the point of intersection of RF with AB. Since F is the midpoint of CB we have $H(C, B, F, P)$. But $C, B, F, P \overset{R}{\underset{\wedge}{=}} A, B, E', Q$, making $H(A, B, E', Q)$. But we already have $H(A, B, E, Q)$. Therefore. $E = E'$ and the points E, F, R are collinear. Hence $EF \parallel AC$.

COROLLARY   *If M is the midpoint of AB then AM is congruent to MB*

DEFINITION 6.27   A *median* of a triangle is a line joining a vertex to the midpoint of the opposite side.

THEOREM 6.27   *The three medians of a triangle are concurrent.*

This is proven by noting that the given triangle and the triangle formed by the midpoints of the three sides, are perspective from a line (l_∞) and therefore are perspective from a point.

The student has no doubt recognized most of the above affine theorems as known Euclidean theorems. Indeed, the set of points in an affine plane is isomorphic to the set of points in a Euclidean plane (see Sec. 6.1). Historically, the set of points in the real projective plane was obtained from the set of points in a Euclidean plane by adding an ideal line (see Sec. 3.1). We have obtained the set of points in the Euclidean plane by deleting a line from the set of points in the projective plane. It can be shown that all of Hilbert's postulates for the Euclidean plane, *except the postulates of congruence*, are valid in an affine plane (Fishback, Sec. 11.2). Hence many

Euclidean theorems are affine theorems. The proofs, of course, are very different since we are using the approach through projective geometry. The vocabulary is often different too. For example, in Euclidean language the non-parallel lines $3x + 2y + 5 = 0$, $2x - 5y + 1 = 0$ have *slopes* $-3/2$ and $2/5$, respectively; while in affine language these lines have *ideal points* $(2, -3, 0)$ and $(5, 2, 0)$, respectively.

Exercises

1. Prove Theorem 6.21 analytically.

2. Prove Theorem 6.22.

3. Prove Theorem 6.23.

4. Prove Theorem 6.24.

5. State Desargues' Theorem in all possible cases applying to the affine plane.

6. Show that Hilbert's axioms of incidence and order are valid in the affine plane.

7. Prove Theorem 6.25.

8. Prove the Corollary to Theorem 6.26.

9. Prove that the diagonals of a parallelogram have the same midpoint.

10. Prove the converse of Exercise 9.

11. If homogeneous parameters of two points on a line are $A(a, 1)$ and $B(b, 1)$ and its ideal point is $(1, 0)$, find homogeneous parameters of the midpoint of AB.

12. If D, E, F are the midpoints of sides BC, CA, AB, respectively, of triangle ABC, show that $H(DE, DF, DA, DB)$.

13. Show that point (x_2, y_2) is between points (x_1, y_1) and (x_3, y_3) if there exists a real number t, $0 < t < 1$, such that $x_2 = (1 - t)x_1 + tx_3$, $y_2 = (1 - t)y_1 + ty_3$.

14. Show that if m and n are distinct lines and if every line which intersects m also intersects n, then m is parallel to n.

15. State Theorem 6.27 in a form that would hold in the projective plane.

6.3   Conics in the Affine Plane

Having singled out a line in the projective plane to be kept invariant, we are now able to distinguish among the conics.

DEFINITION 6.31   A conic is a *hyperbola, parabola,* or *ellipse* according as it contains two, one, or no real ideal points (Fig. 6.31).

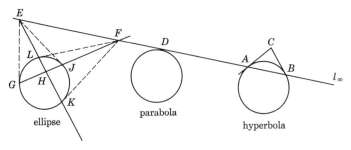

FIG. 6.31

THEOREM 6.31   *The conic*

$$a_{11}x_1{}^2 + 2a_{12}x_1x_2 + a_{22}x_2{}^2 + 2a_{13}x_1x_3 + 2a_{23}x_2x_3 + a_{33}x_2{}^2 = 0$$

represents a hyperbola, parabola, or ellipse according as the discriminant, $\Delta = a_{12}{}^2 - a_{11}a_{22}$, *is greater than, equal to, or less than zero.* (Proof left to the student.)

DEFINITION 6.32   The *center* of a conic is the pole of the ideal line with respect to the conic. The polar of any ideal point with respect to the conic is a *diameter* of the conic. Two diameters are called *conjugate diameters* if the ideal point of one is the pole of the other. A diameter which is its own conjugate is called a *self-conjugate diameter*. (It is tangent to the conic at an ideal point.) A tangent to a conic at an ideal point is also called an *asymptote*.

In Fig. 6.31, AC and BC are asymptotes of the hyperbola, C is the center; D is the center of the parabola; GJ and LK are conjugate diameters of the ellipse, H is the center. The next three theorems follow directly from these definitions.

THEOREM 6.32   *The hyperbola has a center which is an exterior point (Def. 5.67), the ellipse has a center which is an interior point, the parabola has a center on l_∞ and therefore has no center in the affine plane.*

THEOREM 6.33   *The hyperbola is the only conic with real asymptotes (two) in the affine plane. The parabola's single asymptote is l_∞ and therefore not in the affine plane.*

THEOREM 6.34   *The diameters of a conic go through the center. Hence the diameters of a parabola are parallel to each other.*

THEOREM 6.35   *For central conics (ellipse and hyperbola) the center is the midpoint of all chords through it.* (Proof follows from Cor. to Th. 5.67 and the definition of midpoint.)

THEOREM 6.36   *For central conics, the midpoints of all chords parallel to a given diameter lie on the conjugate diameter.*

Let DE be a chord parallel to diameter AB through the center C (Fig. 6.32). Then CQ, which is the diameter conjugate to AB, is the polar of P, the ideal point of the line DE. Hence by the corollary to Theorem 5.67 and the definition of midpoint, M is the midpoint of DE, where $M = DE \cdot CQ$.

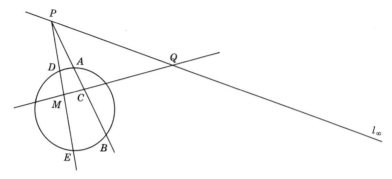

FIG. 6.32

(Figure 6.32 illustrates the theorem using an ellipse. The student should draw the corresponding figure for a hyperbola.)

THEOREM 6.37   *The correspondence between a diameter of a central conic and its conjugate diameter is an involution (Def. 5.43).* (This is obvious from the definitions.)

The involution of Theorem 6.37 induces an involution on l_∞. To find P' on l_∞ which corresponds under the involution to a given point P on l_∞ we proceed as follows (Fig. 6.33): Let p be the polar of P with respect to the

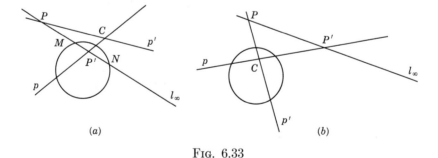

(a)   (b)

FIG. 6.33

conic. Then p is a diameter whose conjugate diameter is line PC where C is the center of the conic. Hence $P' = p \cdot l_\infty$. If the conic is a hyperbola [Fig. 6.33(a)] this involution has two fixed points M and N where the conic intersects l_∞. If the conic is an ellipse [Fig. 6.33(b)] there are no real fixed points. The first is a *hyperbolic*, the second an *elliptic* involution (cf. Def. 5.42).

Exercises

1. Prove Theorem 6.31.

2. Prove Theorem 6.35.

3. Draw the diagram for Theorem 6.36 using a hyperbola.

4. Prove that any conic with two distinct parallel tangents is a central conic.

5. Prove that if a hexagon inscribed in a conic has two pairs of opposite sides parallel, then the third pair of opposite sides are parallel.

6. Classify the following conics and find the center of each. In the case of hyperbolas, find the equations of the asymptotes.

(a) $x_1^2 + 2x_2^2 - 4x_3^2 = 0$

(b) $x_1x_2 - x_3^2 = 0$

(c) $x_1^2 + 4x_2^2 - 6x_1x_3 + 16x_2x_3 + 21x_3^2 = 0$

(d) $x_1^2 - 4x_1x_3 + 3x_2^2 - x_3^2 = 0$

(e) $x_1^2 + x_2^2 - x_3^2 = 0$

(f) $x_1^2 + x_2^2 + x_3^2 = 0$

(g) $x_1^2 - x_2^2 - x_3^2 = 0$

(h) $x_1^2 + 3x_1x_2 - 4x_2^2 + 2x_1x_3 - 10x_2x_3 = 0.$

7. Prove that if a parallelogram is circumscribed about a central conic, its diagonals are conjugate diameters of the conic. (Hint: Use the dual of Th. 5.67.)

8. Let the tangents to an ellipse at two distinct points A and B intersect in point P. Let a tangent parallel to AB intersect PA in point R, PB in point S, and touch the conic at point T. Show that T is the midpoint of RS.

9. Let the tangents to a parabola at two distinct points A and B intersect in point P. Let M be the midpoint of chord AB and let line PM intersect the parabola in point Q. Show that line PM is a diameter and that Q is the midpoint of PM.

10. Show that the asymptotes of a hyperbola are harmonic conjugates with respect to every pair of conjugate diameters of the hyperbola.

References

Busemann and Kelly, Chapter III; Fishback, Chapter 11; Levy, Chapter V; Meserve, Chapter 5; Struik, Chapter 6; Young (2), Chapter IX.

6.4 Similarity Transformations

If we now consider a subset of the affine transformations which leave invariant a certain pairing of points on l_∞, we shall obtain a geometry whose properties are those of Euclidean similarity. We shall define this pairing of points by an elliptic involution E on l_∞, and consider those affine transformations T which leave E invariant. By this we mean that if P and Q are two points on l_∞, which are pairs in the involution E [i.e., $E(P) = Q$)], and if $T(P) = P'$ and $T(Q) = Q'$, then P' and Q' are pairs in the involution E [i.e., $E(P') = Q'$].

DEFINITION 6.41   Let E be a given elliptic involution on l_∞. An affine transformation that leaves E invariant is called a *similarity transformation*. E is called the *absolute involution*. The set of similarity transformations forms a group which is a subgroup of the affine group. The corresponding geometry is called *Euclidean similarity geometry*. Two figures which correspond under a similarity transformation are said to be *similar*.

In the affine plane, we were able to define parallel lines. The introduction of the absolute involution now enables us to define perpendicular lines.

DEFINITION 6.42   Two lines are *perpendicular* if their ideal points are pairs in the absolute involution; i.e., if P and Q are ideal points on lines p and q, respectively, then p is perpendicular to q if and only if $E(P) = Q$.

Note that the absolute involution was chosen as an elliptic involution rather than a hyperbolic one to rule out the possibility of a line being perpendicular to itself.

The following theorems follow from the definitions above and their proofs are left to the student:

THEOREM 6.41   *Perpendicularity is an invariant relation under similarity transformations; i.e., if p is perpendicular to q, then p' is perpendicular to q' where p' and q' correspond to p and q, respectively, under a similarity transformation.*

THEOREM 6.42   *Through any point P there exists one and only one line m' perpendicular to a given line m.*

THEOREM 6.43   *A line perpendicular to one of two parallel lines is perpendicular to the other.*

THEOREM 6.44   *Two distinct lines which are perpendicular to the same line are parallel to each other.*

To find an analytic expression for a similarity transformation we start with an affine transformation T given by

$$\delta x_1' = a_{11}x_1 + a_{12}x_2 + a_{12}x_3$$
$$\delta x_2' = a_{21}x_1 + a_{22}x_2 + a_{23}x_3 \qquad |a_{ij}| \neq 0.$$
$$\delta x_3' = \qquad\qquad\qquad\quad x_3$$

Since for every point on l_∞, $x_3 = 0$, the absolute involution involves only x_1 and x_2. Let E be the involution on l_∞ given by the equations $\delta x_1' = x_2$, $\delta x_2' = -x_1$. (Note that this makes the line $x_1 = 0$ perpendicular to line $x_2 = 0$, since the ideal point $(0, 1, 0)$ of the first line corresponds under E to the ideal point $(1, 0, 0)$ of the second. In non-homogeneous coordinates these are the lines $x = 0$ and $y = 0$ of a *rectangular coordinate system*.)

Let $P(x_1, x_2, 0)$ be any point on l_∞. Then $E(P) = Q(x_2, -x_1, 0)$.

Now $T(P) = P'$ and $T(Q) = Q'$ where we see by substituting in the equations of the transformation T that

$$P' \text{ is point } (a_{11}x_1 + a_{12}x_2,\ a_{21}x_1 + a_{22}x_2,\ 0) \text{ and}$$

$$Q' \text{ is point } (a_{11}x_2 - a_{12}x_1,\ a_{21}x_2 - a_{22}x_1,\ 0).$$

For E to be invariant we want $E(P') = Q'$. We therefore seek conditions on the coefficients of T so that the following two equations are satisfied for *all* x_1 and x_2, not both zero:

$$\delta(a_{11}x_2 - a_{12}x_1) = a_{21}x_1 + a_{22}x_2$$

$$\delta(a_{21}x_2 - a_{22}x_1) = -(a_{11}x_1 + a_{12}x_2).$$

These equations are equivalent to the following:

$$(a_{21} + a_{12}\delta)x_1 + (a_{22} - a_{11}\delta)x_2 = 0$$

$$(a_{11} - a_{22}\delta)x_1 + (a_{12} + a_{21}\delta)x_2 = 0.$$

For these to hold for *all* x_1 and x_2, all four coefficients of x_1 and x_2 must equal zero; i.e., we have the following:

$$(a_{21} + a_{12}\delta) = 0$$

$$(a_{22} - a_{11}\delta) = 0$$

$$(a_{11} - a_{22}\delta) = 0$$

$$(a_{12} + a_{21}\delta) = 0.$$

From the first and fourth of these equations we have

$$\delta = -a_{21}/a_{12} = -a_{12}/a_{21}.$$

Therefore $\delta^2 = 1$, $\delta = \pm 1$, and $a_{12} = \mp a_{21}$.

From the second and third equations we have

$$\delta = a_{22}/a_{11} = a_{11}/a_{22}.$$

Therefore $\delta^2 = 1$, $\delta = \pm 1$, and $a_{11} = \pm a_{22}$.

We therefore have two types of similarity transformation.

DEFINITION 6.43 A *direct similarity transformation* is an affine transformation where $a_{11} = a_{22}$, $a_{12} = -a_{21}$, yielding the equations

$$\delta x_1' = a_{11}x_1 - a_{12}x_2 + a_{13}x_3$$

$$\delta x_2' = a_{12}x_1 + a_{11}x_2 + a_{23}x_3 \qquad (a_{11}{}^2 + a_{12}{}^2) \neq 0.$$

$$\delta x_3' = x_3$$

In non-homogeneous form these equations take the form

$$x' = ax - by + c$$
$$y' = bx + ay + d \qquad (a^2 + b^2) \neq 0.$$

An *indirect similarity transformation* is an affine transformation where $a_{11} = -a_{22}$, and $a_{12} = a_{21}$, yielding the equations

$$\delta x_1' = a_{11}x_1 + a_{12}x_2 + a_{13}x_3$$
$$\delta x_2' = a_{12}x_1 - a_{11}x_2 + a_{23}x_3 \qquad (a_{11}{}^2 + a_{12}{}^2) \neq 0.$$
$$\delta x_3' = \qquad\qquad\quad x_3$$

In non-homogeneous coordinates these equations take the form

$$x' = ax + by + c$$
$$y' = bx - ay + d \qquad (a^2 + b^2) \neq 0.$$

DEFINITION 6.44 The indirect similarity transformation $x' = x$, $y' = -y$ is called a *reflection in the x-axis*.

Note that an indirect similarity transformation is the product of a direct similarity transformation and a reflection in the x-axis.

THEOREM 6.45 *The product of two indirect similarity transformations is a direct similarity transformation.* (Proof left to student.) *Hence the set of indirect similarity transformations does not form a group.*

THEOREM 6.46 *The set of direct and indirect similarity transformations forms a group of which the set of direct similarity transformations is a subgroup.* (Proof is left to the student.)

THEOREM 6.47 *There exist exactly two similarity transformations, one direct and one indirect, under which a pair of distinct points A, B corresponds to a pair of distinct points A', B' respectively.*

(Proof left to student: Use non-homogeneous coordinates. Substituting the coordinates of A and A', B and B' into the transformation equations gives four linear equations in the four unknowns a, b, c, d. The solutions will be unique because $A \neq B$, and $A' \neq B'$.)

Theorem 6.41 established perpendicularity as a similarity invariant. We now wish to introduce a general angle measure which is invariant under similarity transformations and hence will enable us to speak of congruence

of angles. For this we shall need the following property of real numbers:
Schwarz's inequality: For any four real numbers a, b, c, d,

$$|ac + bd| \leq (a^2 + b^2)^{1/2} (c^2 + d^2)^{1/2}.$$

To prove this we note first that $(ad - bc)^2 \geq 0$. Therefore

$$2abcd \leq a^2d^2 + b^2c^2.$$

Adding $(a^2c^2 + b^2d^2)$ to both sides and factoring gives us

$$(ac + bd)^2 \leq (a^2 + b^2)(c^2 + d^2)$$

from which Schwarz's inequality follows.

The measure of an angle will now be defined as follows:

DEFINITION 6.45   To every pair of ordinary lines $[u_1, u_2, u_3]$ and $[v_1, v_2, v_3]$ there corresponds a non-negative real number denoted by $\cos \theta$, and given by

$$\cos \theta = \frac{|u_1v_1 + u_2v_2|}{(u_1{}^2 + u_2{}^2)^{1/2} (v_1{}^2 + v_2{}^2)^{1/2}}.$$

θ is called the *acute angle between the two lines.*

From Schwartz's inequality, it is clear that $0 \leq \cos \theta \leq 1$. Note that $\cos \theta$ is not to be considered as having any significance as a ratio of lengths. It is here considered simply as a real number given by the definition. We could define θ as the real number for which $\cos \theta$ is the sum of the infinite series:

$$\cos \theta = 1 - \frac{\theta^2}{2!} + \frac{\theta^4}{4!} - \frac{\theta^6}{6!} \cdots$$

and then have θ such that $0 \leq \theta \leq \pi/2$.

THEOREM 6.48   *Cos θ is invariant under similarity transformations.*

The proof for direct similarity follows:

Take the lines $u_1'x' + u_2'y' + u_3' = 0$,

$$v_1'x' + v_2'y' + v_3' = 0.$$

Under direct similarity transformations these equations become

$$u_1'(ax - by + c) + u_2'(bx + ay + d) + u_3' = 0,$$

$$v_1'(ax - by + c) + v_2'(bx + ay + d) + v_3' = 0.$$

These may be written as $u_1 x + u_2 y + u_3 = 0$

$$v_1 x + v_2 y + v_3 = 0 \text{ where}$$

$$u_1 = u_1' a + u_2' b \qquad v_1 = v_1' a + v_2' b$$

$$u_2 = u_2' a - u_1' b \qquad v_2 = v_2' a - v_1' b.$$

Then some elementary algebraic manipulation will show that

$$\frac{|u_1 v_1 + u_2 v_2|}{(u_1{}^2 + u_2{}^2)^{1/2} (v_1{}^2 + v_2{}^2)^{1/2}} = \frac{|u_1' v_1' + u_2' v_2'|}{(u_1'{}^2 + u_2'{}^2)^{1/2} (v_1'{}^2 + v_2'{}^2)^{1/2}}.$$

DEFINITION 6.46   Two acute angles θ_1 and θ_2 are *congruent* if $\cos \theta_1 = \cos \theta_2$. Thus congruence of angles is a similarity invariant.

The following theorem relates perpendicularity (Def. 6.42) to angle measure (Def. 6.45):

THEOREM 6.49   *Two lines are perpendicular if and only if* $\cos \theta = 0$.

Let the two lines be

$$u_1 x_1 + u_2 x_2 + u_3 x_3 = 0 \qquad \text{with ideal point } (u_2, -u_1, 0)$$

$$v_1 x_1 + v_2 x_2 + v_3 x_3 = 0 \qquad \text{with ideal point } (v_2, -v_1, 0).$$

Part I: If these lines are perpendicular, then their ideal points correspond under the absolute involution; i.e., $\delta v_2 = -u_1$, and $\delta v_1 = u_2$. Therefore,

$$u_1 v_1 + u_2 v_2 = \delta(-v_1 v_2 + v_1 v_2) = 0,$$

making $\cos \theta = 0$.

Part II: If $\cos \theta = 0$, then $u_1 v_1 + u_2 v_2 = 0$.

Therefore $-u_1/v_2 = u_2/v_1$. Setting these ratios equal to δ gives $\delta v_2 = -u_1$, and $\delta v_1 = u_2$, making the two lines perpendicular.

Exercises

1. Show that for points on l_∞, $ET = TE$ where T is an affine transformation which leaves the absolute involution E invariant.

2. Prove Theorem 6.41.

3. Prove Theorem 6.42.

4. Prove Theorem 6.43.

5. Prove Theorem 6.44.

6. Show that in general a direct similarity transformation has exactly one fixed point in the affine plane. What is the exception?

7. Prove Theorem 6.45.

8. Prove Theorem 6.46.

9. Prove Theorem 6.47.

10. Given four points with non-homogeneous coordinates $A(4, -5)$, $B(1, 2)$, $C(5, -4)$, $D(2, 1)$, determine the two similarity transformations such that $T(A) = B$, $T(C) = D$.

11. Show that Euclidean distance $[(x_2 - x_1)^2 + (y_2 - y_1)^2]^{1/2}$ is not invariant under a general similarity transformation.

12. Show that all lines perpendicular to the line $ax_1 + bx_2 + cx_3 = 0$ are expressible in the form $bx_1 - ax_2 + dx_3 = 0$.

13. Show that if two acute angles have their corresponding sides parallel then they are congruent.

14. Show that the lines whose non-homogeneous equations are $y = m_1x + b$ and $y = m_2x + c$ are perpendicular if and only if $m_2 = -1/m_1$.

15. Define altitude of a triangle. Show that the altitudes of triangle ABC are concurrent when $A = (0, 0, 1)$, $B = (1, 0, 1)$, $C = (a, b, 1)$.

16. If, instead of choosing an *elliptic* involution on l_∞ as the absolute involution, we choose a *hyperbolic* one, we obtain the two-dimensional case of *Minkowski's geometry* of space–time used by Einstein for the special theory of relativity. Take the hyperbolic involution $\delta x_1' = x_2$, $\delta x_2' = x_1$ as the absolute involution and derive the analytic representation of the resulting transformations. Show these form a group. [For more on Minkowski's geometry, the student is referred to A. A. Robb, *Geometry of Time and Space* (Cambridge University Press, New York, 1936).]

6.5   Homothetic Transformations

DEFINITION 6.51   A similarity transformation that leaves l_∞ pointwise invariant is called a *homothetic transformation*.

For the analytic representation of a homothetic transformation we start with a direct similarity transformation S

$$\delta x_1' = a_{11}x_1 - a_{12}x_2 + a_{13}x_3$$
$$\delta x_2' = a_{12}x_1 + a_{11}x_2 + a_{23}x_3 \qquad (a_{11}^2 + a_{12}^2) \neq 0.$$
$$\delta x_3' = \qquad\qquad\qquad\qquad x_3$$

Let $P(x_1, x_2, 0)$ be any point on l_∞. Then $S(P)$ has the coordinates $(a_{11}x_1 - a_{12}x_2, a_{12}x_1 + a_{11}x_2, 0)$. We want $S(P) = P$. We therefore seek conditions on the coefficients such that the following equations are satisfied for *all* values of x_1 and x_2:

$$a_{11}x_1 - a_{12}x_2 = kx_1$$
$$\qquad\qquad\qquad\qquad k \neq 0.$$
$$a_{12}x_1 + a_{11}x_2 = kx_2$$

Therefore $a_{12} = 0$, $a_{11} = k \neq 0$, and a homothetic transformation is given by the equations

$$\delta x_1' = a_{11}x_1 + a_{13}x_3$$
$$\delta x_2' = a_{11}x_2 + a_{23}x_3 \qquad a_{11} \neq 0.$$
$$\delta x_3' = \qquad\qquad\qquad x_3$$

In non-homogeneous coordinates these take the form

$$x' = ax + c$$
$$y' = ay + d$$
$$a \neq 0.$$

THEOREM 6.51   *The set of homothetic transformations forms a group.* (Proof left to student.)

THEOREM 6.52   *Under a homothetic transformation a line p corresponds to a line p' which is parallel to p.* (Proof left to student.)

THEOREM 6.53   *Under the homothetic transformation $x' = ax + c$, $y' = ay + d$, $a \neq 0$, one ordinary point is left invariant if $a \neq 1$. If $a = 1$ the only invariant points are on l_∞, unless the transformation is the identity transformation.*

To prove this theorem we set $x = ax + c$, and $y = ay + d$, and obtain $x = c/(1 - a)$, $y = d/(1 - a)$, as the coordinates of the invariant point. This is an ordinary point if $a \neq 1$.

DEFINITION 6.52   In the homothetic transformation of Theorem 6.53, if $a = 1$ the transformation is called a *translation;* if $a \neq 1$ it is called a *dilation.*

THEOREM 6.54   *The set of translations forms a group, but the set of dilations does not.* (Proof left to student.)

THEOREM 6.55   *A translation is completely determined by an ordinary point and its corresponding point; i.e., there exists a unique translation under which a given point P corresponds to a given point Q.* (Proof left to student: see hint for proof of Theorem 6.47.)

THEOREM 6.56   *Under a dilation all lines through the invariant point are invariant lines (not pointwise invariant).*

This follows from the fact that each such line has two invariant points, its ideal point and the given ordinary point. Thus if F is the invariant point of a dilation T and if P is any other point in the affine plane, then F, P, and $T(P)$ are collinear (Fig. 6.51).

Note that a dilation is a homology (Def. 5.53) whose axis is l_∞, and whose center is the fixed point of the dilation. Another homology of importance is the following:

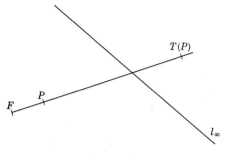

FIG. 6.51

DEFINITION 6.53   An *orthogonal line reflection* is a harmonic homology (Def. 5.54) whose center M is on l_∞ and whose axis m intersects l_∞ at a point N which corresponds to M under the absolute involution [i.e., $E(M) = N$].

THEOREM 6.57   *Under an orthogonal line reflection with center M and axis m a point P is transformed into a point P' such that the line PP' is perpendicular to m and intersects m at the midpoint R of segment PP' (Fig. 6.52).*

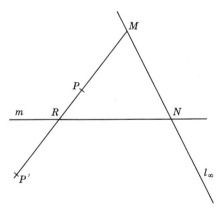

FIG. 6.52

The proof is an immediate consequence of the definitions involved; i.e., Definitions 5.54, 6.26, and 6.53.

COROLLARY   *A reflection in the x-axis (Def. 6.44) is an orthogonal line reflection whose axis is the x-axis and whose center is $Y(0, 1, 0)$.*

Exercises

1. Show that an indirect similarity transformation cannot be a homothetic transformation.

2. Prove Theorem 6.51.

3. Prove Theorem 6.52.

4. Prove Theorem 6.54.

5. Prove Theorem 6.55.

6. In the homothetic transformation of Theorem 6.53, if $a = -1$ the transformation is called a *central reflection*. Show that the product of the two central reflections is a translation.

7. Show that the group of translations is commutative, but that the group of general homothetic transformations is not.

8. Given two dilations T_1 and T_2 with the same fixed point (Def. 6.52). Find unique point P such that $T_1(P) = T_2(P)$.

9. Show that the square of an indirect similarity transformation is a dilation.

10. Prove Theorem 6.57 and its corollary.

6.6   The Euclidean Metric Plane

To obtain the familiar metric properties of the Euclidean plane there remains the problem of finding some way of defining congruence which will generalize the very limited concept defined for the affine plane (Sec. 6.2). We do this by introducing a special *distance function* or *metric* into the affine plane and then considering the transformations that keep this metric invariant.

We start with the concept of an abstract metric space.

DEFINITION 6.61   A *metric space* is a set of elements P_i such that to each ordered pair of elements there corresponds a non-negative real number $d(P_1P_2)$, called the *distance* P_1P_2, satisfying the following conditions:

(1) $d(P_1P_2) = 0$ if and only if $P_1 = P_2$

(2) $d(P_1P_2) = d(P_2P_1)$

(3) $d(P_1P_2) + d(P_2P_3) \geqq d(P_1P_3)$.

DEFINITION 6.62   The *Euclidean metric plane* is the set of points in the affine plane together with the following distance function or metric: If (x_1, y_1) and (x_2, y_2) are non-homogeneous coordinates of two ordinary points P_1 and P_2, then

$$d(P_1P_2) = \sqrt{(x_2 - x_1)^2 + (y_2 - y_1)^2}.$$

DEFINITION 6.63   Two line segments AB and CD are *congruent* if $d(AB) = d(CD)$.

We must show that the Euclidean metric satisfies the three conditions of Definition 6.61. The first two are left to the student. For the third condition, some elementary algebraic manipulation will show that $[d(P_1P_2) + d(P_2P_3)]^2 - [d(P_1P_3)]^2$ is equal to

$$*2\sqrt{(x_2 - x_1)^2 + (y_2 - y_1)^2} \cdot \sqrt{(x_3 - x_2)^2 + (y_3 - y_2)^2}$$
$$-2\,[(x_2 - x_1)(x_3 - x_2) + (y_2 - y_1)(y_3 - y_2)]*$$

Now if we let $a = (x_2 - x_1)$, $b = (y_2 - y_1)$, $c = (x_3 - x_2)$, $d = (y_3 - y_2)$, we see from Schwarz's inequality (Sec. 6.4) that the first term in the starred expression above is greater than or equal to the absolute value of the second. Therefore

$$[d(P_1P_2) + d(P_2P_3)]^2 - [d(P_1P_3)]^2 \geqq 0$$

and the third condition, known as the triangle inequality, holds.

Note that we obtain the *Euclidean* metric plane by specifying a *particular* distance function. We could obtain *other* metric planes by starting with other elements P_i and/or other distance functions. See, for example, Ex. 2 and 3 at the end of this section and also Chapter 7.

THEOREM 6.61   *If two segments are congruent by Definition 6.25, they are also congruent by Definition 6.63.*

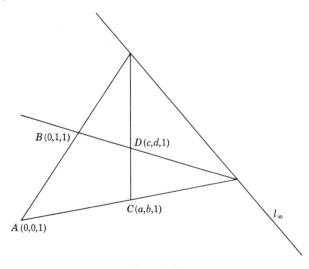

FIG. 6.61

For this we must show that the opposite sides of a parallelogram are congruent by Def. 6.63. Let the coordinate system be chosen so that $A = (0, 0, 1)$ and $B = (0, 1, 1)$. Then $C = (a, b, 1)$ and $D = (c, d, 1)$ with conditions on the coordinates to be determined by $AB \parallel CD$, and $AC \parallel BD$. Now AB is line $[1, 0, 0]$ and CD is line $[d - b, a - c, cb - ad]$, giving $a = c$. Line $AC = [b, -a, 0]$ and $BD = [d - 1, -c, c]$ giving $b = d - 1$. Thus if $C = (a, b, 1)$ then $D = (a, b + 1, 1)$ and direct substitution yields $d(AC) = d(BD)$ and $d(AB) = d(CD)$.

Exercises

1. Show that the Euclidean metric satisfies the first two conditions of Definitions 6.61.

2. Show that the following are metric spaces:
(a) The set of points $P_i(x_i, y_i)$ in the affine plane with $d(P_1P_2) = |x_2 - x_1| + |y_2 - y_1|$.
(b) The same set with $d(P_1P_2) = \max (|x_2 - x_1|, |y_2 - y_1|)$.

3. If O is the origin in a rectangular coordinate system in the spaces of Ex.1, describe the "unit circle" in each; i.e., the locus of point P such that $d(OP) = 1$.

4. Show that the following is not a metric space: The set of points $P_i(x_i)$ on a line with $d(P_1P_2) = |x_2^2 - x_1^2|$.

5. Show that if P_2 is between P_1 and P_3 then $d(P_1P_2) + d(P_2P_3) = d(P_1P_3)$ (see Ex. 13, Sec. 6.2).

6. Show that under the dilation $T: x' = ax + c, y' = ay + d, a \neq 1$, Euclidean distances are multiplied by the constant a. Thus if F is the fixed point of T, and P is any point in the Euclidean metric plane, then $T(P) = P'$ on line FP (Th. 6.56) such that $d(FP') = a \cdot d(FP)$.

7. Show that under the translation $T: x' = x + c, y' = y + d$, the Euclidean metric is invariant.

8. Show that under a reflection in the x-axis (Def. 6.44), the Euclidean metric is invariant.

6.7 Isometries of the Euclidean Plane

We now seek the transformations that keep Euclidean distance invariant. The general affine transformation does not (Ex. 3 of Sec. 6.1); neither does the general similarity transformation (Ex. 11 of Sec. 6.4). The following theorem will lead us to the required transformations.

THEOREM 6.71 *Under a similarity transformation S, Euclidean distances are multiplied by a constant r; i.e., if $S(P_1) = P_1'$ and $S(P_2) = P_2'$ then the ratio $d(P_1'P_2')/d(P_1P_2)$ is constant for S.*

The proof will be given for a direct similarity transformation. The proof for an indirect one is left to the student.

$$d(P_1'P_2') = \sqrt{(x_2' - x_1')^2 + (y_2' - y_1')^2} \quad \text{where}$$

$$x_1' = ax_1 - by_1 + c \quad x_2' = ax_2 - by_2 + c \quad (a^2 + b^2) \neq 0.$$
$$y_1' = bx_1 + ay_1 + d \quad y_2' = bx_2 + ay_2 + d$$

Substituting these values and simplifying, we get

$$d(P_1'P_2') = \sqrt{(a^2 + b^2)(x_2 - x_1)^2 + (a^2 + b^2)(y_2 - y_1)^2}$$
$$= (a^2 + b^2)^{1/2} \cdot d(P_1P_2). \text{ Hence } r = (a^2 + b^2)^{1/2}.$$

COROLLARY *Under the similarity group the ratio of two distances is invariant.*

DEFINITION 6.71 A similarity transformation which keeps distance invariant is a *rigid motion* or *isometry.* The study of properties invariant under these isometries is called *Euclidean Metric Geometry.* Two figures which correspond to each other under an isometry are said to be *congruent.*

DEFINITION 6.72 An isometry which is a direct similarity transformation is called a *displacement;* an isometry which is an indirect similarity transformation is called a *symmetry.*

From Theorem 6.71 we see that isometries have the following analytic forms:

Displacements
$$x' = ax - by + c$$
$$y' = bx + ay + d$$
where $a^2 + b^2 = 1$

Symmetries
$$x' = ax + by + c$$
$$y' = bx - ay + d$$
where $a^2 + b^2 = 1.$

The next two theorems are left to the student to prove.

THEOREM 6.72 *The set of isometries forms a group of which the set of displacements forms a subgroup.*

THEOREM 6.73 *The set of translations (Def. 6.52) is a subgroup of the group of displacements.*

THEOREM 6.74 *Under a translation T, any point A is transformed into a point A' such that (1) $d(AA')$ is the same for all points A and (2) all lines AA' have the same ideal point; i.e., a translation may be said to "move" all points the same distance along parallel lines (Fig. 6.71).*

Let T be given by $x' = x + c$, $y' = y + d$. If A_1 is the point (x_1, y_1) then A_1' is the point $(x_1 + c, y_1 + d)$. Thus $d(A_1A_1')$ is $(c^2 + d^2)^{1/2}$ which is independent of the coordinates of A. This proves condition (1). For (2) use homogeneous coordinates. Thus $A_1 = (x_1, y_1, 1)$ and $A_1' = (x_1 + c,$

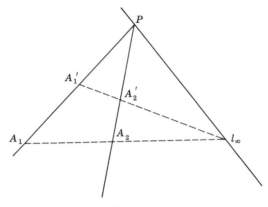

FIG. 6.71

$y_1 + d$, 1), making line $A_1A_1' = [-d, c, x_1d - y_1c]$. The ideal point of A_1A_1' is $(c, d, 0)$ (Th. 6.13), which is independent of A.

DEFINITION 6.73   A displacement which leaves an ordinary point invariant is called a *rotation* whose *center* is the invariant point.

THEOREM 6.75   *A rotation with center (h, k) is given by*

$$x' = a(x - h) - b(y - k) + h$$
$$y' = b(x - h) + a(y - k) + k \qquad a^2 + b^2 = 1.$$

(Proof left to student: In the equations for a displacement let $x' = x = h$, and $y' = y = k$, and solve for c and d).

COROLLARY   *A rotation with center $(0, 0)$ is given by*

$$x' = ax - by$$
$$y' = bx + ay \qquad a^2 + b^2 = 1.$$

THEOREM 6.76   *Under a rotation R with center $(0, 0)$ a point A is transformed into a point A' such that (1) $d(OA) = d(OA')$ and (2) the angle between OA and OA' is the same for all points A; i.e., a rotation may be said to "move" all points through the same angle along arcs of concentric circles with center at O (Fig. 6.72).*

Let R be given by the equations of the Corollary to Theorem 6.75. Condition (1) holds because O is a fixed point of R and R is an isometry. For condition (2) we use Definition 6.45. In homogeneous coordinates $A = (x_1, y_1, 1)$, $A_1' = (ax_1 - by_1, bx_1 + ay_1, 1)$ and $O = (0, 0, 1)$. Then line

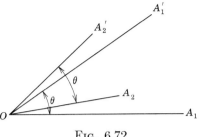

FIG. 6.72

$OA = [y_1, -x_1, 0]$ and $OA' = [bx_1 + ay_1, by_1 - ax_1, 0]$. Substituting in the definition for $\cos \theta$ and simplifying, we get

$$\cos \theta = \frac{a(x_1{}^2 + y_1{}^2)}{d(OA) \cdot d(OA')} = a$$

which is independent of the point A.

Note that if in the equations of the Corollary to Theorem 6.75, we set $a = \cos \theta$, then $b = \sin \theta$ and we obtain the familiar form for a rotation through an angle θ about the origin:

$$x' = x \cos \theta - y \sin \theta$$
$$y' = x \sin \theta + y \cos \theta.$$

THEOREM 6.77 *An orthogonal line reflection (Def. 6.53) is an isometry.*

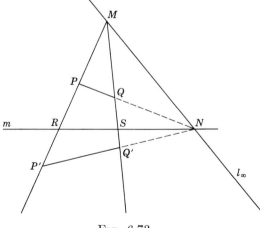

FIG. 6.73

Let M and m be the center and axis of the given reflection (Fig. 6.73). Then if P and Q are any two ordinary points, the corresponding points P'

and Q' are such that PP' and QQ' are perpendicular to m (Th. 6.57), thus making $PP' \parallel QQ'$. Also by Theorem 6.57, we have $H(P, P', M, R)$ and $H(Q, Q', M, S)$. We must prove that PQ is congruent to $P'Q'$. This can be done by showing that $PQ \parallel P'Q'$ and then applying Theorem 6.61.

We summarize the isometries of the Euclidean plane in a final theorem whose proof is left to the student.

THEOREM 6.78   *A displacement may be expressed as the product of a rotation with center $(0, 0)$ and a translation; a symmetry may be expressed as the product of a rotation with center $(0, 0)$, a translation, and a reflection in the x-axis.*

The isometries of the Euclidean plane consist of rotations, translations, line reflections, and their products. In fact, it can be shown that any rotation is the product of two reflections as is also any translation. Hence any isometry is a product of reflections alone (Levi, Chap. 9).

By means of these isometries, we can develop all the properties of Euclidean geometry. For example, we can show that two triangles are congruent if two sides and the included angle of one are congruent respectively to two sides and the included angle of the other, by exhibiting an isometry which transforms one triangle into the other. However, having shown how Euclidean geometry is obtained as a subgeometry of projective geometry, we do not plan to go further. For a full development of Euclidean geometry and trigonometry on this basis, the student is referred to the book by Levi listed in the bibliography. In the next two chapters, we shall assume the elementary properties of Euclidean geometry and trigonometry wherever we need them.

Exercises

1. Prove Theorem 6.72.
2. Show that the group of displacements is not commutative.
3. Prove Theorem 6.73.
4. Complete the proof of Theorem 6.75.
5. Prove that the set of rotations with a given center forms a commutative group.
6. Complete the proof of Theorem 6.77.
7. Prove Theorem 6.78.
8. Find the equations of the displacement under which points $(2, 4)$ and $(-1, 5)$ correspond to $(4, 2)$ and $(3, 5)$, respectively.
9. Show that the product of a rotation and a translation is a rotation through the same angle as the first rotation but with a different center.
10. Prove that triangle ABC is congruent to triangle DEF if AB is congruent to DE, AC is congruent to DF, and angle A is congruent to angle D.

ERRATUM FOR

A MODERN INTRODUCTION
TO
GEOMETRIES

by
Annita Tuller

*On page 128, the conclusion of the first paragraph (line four)
should read and continue as follows:*

be done by showing that $PQ \parallel P'Q'$ and then applying Theorem 6.61, if
$PQ \parallel m$. For the general case the theorem may be proven analytically by
choosing the coordinate system so that m has the equation $x_2 = 0$.

6.8 Summary

The work of this chapter may be summed up in the following diagram of the genealogy of linear transformations:

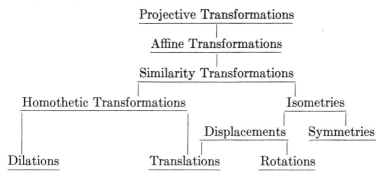

Since the invariants of a group are also invariants of any subgroup, a subgeometry has the properties of the parent geometry for the point set that they have in common. For example, the projective properties of collinearity and cross-ratio of four elements in a pencil are preserved in the subgroups of the projective group; but the projective property that two lines determine a point, is not always valid in the affine plane because the projective plane contains a line which is not present in the affine plane.

We have seen also that because of this deleted line we can distinguish three types of conics in the affine plane, while in the projective plane all conics have the same properties. However, from the projective properties of conics are obtained the properties that are common to *all three* types of conics in the affine plane.

On the other hand, we have seen that as a result of the fact that there are invariants of a subgroup which are not invariants of the parent group, the subgeometry has properties which have no meaning in the parent geometry. For example, the congruence properties in the Euclidean plane have no meaning in the affine plane; the parallelism properties of the affine plane have no meaning in the projective plane. Therefore, in order to classify definitions and theorems as belonging to a particular geometry, we shall assign to a geometry only those properties invariant under its group of transformations, which are not invariant under any larger group. Thus, for example, we shall classify parallelism as an affine property rather than a Euclidean one. In this way, we can state definitely whether a given theorem belongs to a given geometry.

Exercises

1. To which geometry do the following figures belong: (a) triangle, (b) right triangle, (e) equilateral triangle, (d) quadrilateral, (e) parallelogram, (f) rectangle,

(g) rhombus, (h) conic, (i) ellipse, (j) circle, (k) tangent to a conic, (l) a horizontal line? Give the definition in each case.

2. To which geometry do the following theorems belong: (a) Two lines determine a point; (b) three points determine a circle; (c) five points determine a conic; (d) the altitudes of a triangle are concurrent; (e) the medians of a triangle are concurrent; (f) if two triangles are similar, their corresponding sides are parallel; (g) the diagonals of a parallelogram bisect each other; (h) the diagonals of a rectangle bisect each other?

References

Adler, Chap. 11; Coxeter (3) Chap. 3; Fishback, Chap. 11; Graustein, Chap. VII; Levi, Chap. 9; Meserve, Chap. 6; Woods, end of Chap. VI; Young (2) Chap. IX.

CHAPTER 7

PROJECTIVE METRIC GEOMETRIES

In this chapter we shall indicate briefly how the non-Euclidean geometries of Chapter 1 can be developed as subgeometries of projective geometry by introducing a metric into the projective plane in terms of a conic to be kept invariant. If the conic is determined by a hyperbolic polarity (Def. 5.69) we obtain hyperbolic geometry; if the conic is determined by an elliptic polarity we obtain elliptic geometry. Euclidean geometry can be considered as a limiting case of either and is often referred to as parabolic geometry. Although we are concerned only with the *real* hyperbolic and elliptic planes, it will be necessary to introduce non-real points and lines to aid our development.

7.1 Introduction: Laguerre's Projective Interpretation of the Euclidean Angle Between Two Lines

Laguerre, in 1853, was the first to show the relation between the Euclidean concept of angle measure and the projective concept of cross-ratio. In order to present this we shall extend our definitions of points and lines in the projective plane to include non-real points and lines. An elementary knowledge of complex numbers is assumed.

DEFINITION 7.11 A *complex point* is a class of ordered triples of complex numbers (x_1, x_2, x_3), not all zero, where the point $(x_1, x_2, x_3) = (kx_1, kx_2, kx_3)$ for any complex number $k \neq 0$. The complex point is said to be *real* if it has one set of real homogeneous coordinates.

For example, the point $(1 - i, 0, 2 - 2i)$ is equal to the point $(1, 0, 2)$ and is therefore a real point. A non-real complex point will be referred to as an *imaginary point*. We introduce a similar definition for a *complex line*, $[u_1, u_2, u_3]$. A point and line are incident if and only if $u_1x_1 + u_2x_2 + u_3x_3 = 0$. This equation is either the line equation of the point (x_1, x_2, x_3) or the point equation of the line $[u_1, u_2, u_3]$. For example, $x_3 = 0$ is the real line with coordinates $[0, 0, 1]$; $u_1 + iu_2 = 0$ is the imaginary point $(1, i, 0)$. Two points

131

(x_1, x_2, x_3) and (y_1, y_2, y_3) are called *conjugate complex points* if and only if
*$(\bar{x}_1, \bar{x}_2, \bar{x}_3) = (y_1, y_2, y_3)$. A similar definition applies to complex lines.
The following properties are easily verified:

THEOREM 7.11 *If a point (x_1, x_2, x_3) is on line $[u_1, u_2, u_3]$, the conjugate
complex point $(\bar{x}_1, \bar{x}_2, \bar{x}_3)$ is on the conjugate complex line $[\bar{u}_1, \bar{u}_2, \bar{u}_3]$. Hence
if an imaginary point lies on a real line, its conjugate complex point also lies
on this line; and if an imaginary line goes through a real point, the conjugate complex line also goes through this point.*

THEOREM 7.12 *The point of intersection of two conjugate complex lines is a
real point; and the join of two conjugate complex points is a real line.*

THEOREM 7.13 *There is one and only one real line through an imaginary
point; and there is one and only one real point on an imaginary line.*

Note that a *real* line, as defined in this chapter, is a line with *real* homogeneous coordinates. It has an infinite number of both real *and* imaginary
points. For example, the line $x_3 = 0$ has coordinate $[0, 0, 1]$ and is therefore
a real line. It contains imaginary points $(1, i, 0)$, $(2, i, 0)$, $(1, -i, 0)$, etc.
An *imaginary* line, however, contains an infinite number of imaginary points
but only *one* real point (Th. 7.13).

THEOREM 7.14 *A projectivity, with real coefficients, on a real line has two
distinct real invariant points, two coincident real invariant points, or two
conjugate imaginary invariant points (cf. Th. 5.43).*

Now consider the absolute involution of Section 6.4:

$$\delta x_1' = x_2, \quad \delta x_2' = -x_1.$$

Its invariant points are given by the equation $x_1^2 + x_2^2 = 0$. Since these
are on line $x_3 = 0$, the invariant points are the conjugate imaginary points
$(i, 1, 0)$ and $(-i, 1, 0)$, designated by I and J, respectively.

DEFINITION 7.12 The points I and J are called the *circular points at
infinity.*

They were discovered by Poncelet in 1813 while he was a prisoner of war in
Russia after Napoleon's retreat. The reasons for the name will appear in
what follows.

---

*The symbol $\bar{x}$ represents the complex number conjugate to x; i.e., if $x = a + bi$, then
$\bar{x} = a - bi$.

First we note that an ellipse with real coefficients has two conjugate imaginary ideal points (Def. and Th. 6.31). If we define the special ellipse in the Euclidean plane, a circle, as the locus of points a given distance r from a given point (h, k) we obtain the equation $(x - h)^2 + (y - k)^2 = r^2$. The next two theorems then explain why I and J are called the circular points at infinity.

THEOREM 7.15   *All Euclidean circles have ideal points I and J.*

In homogeneous coordinates the equation of a circle becomes $x_1^2 + x_2^2 + 2Dx_1x_3 + 2Ex_2x_3 + Fx_3^2 = 0$. The points of intersection of this with the line $x_3 = 0$ are the points I and J.

THEOREM 7.16   *In the Euclidean plane, any conic with real coefficients which has ideal points I and J, is a circle.*

Consider a conic $Ax_1^2 + 2Bx_1x_2 + Cx_2^2 + 2Dx_1x_3 + 2Ex_2x_3 + Fx_3^2 = 0$ with real coefficients. If this has ideal points I and J then $A - 2Bi - C = 0$, and $A + 2Bi - C = 0$. Therefore $A = C$ and $B = 0$ and the conic is a circle.

From the two theorems above it would seem that points I and J are equidistant from *all* points of the Euclidean plane and that the distance is infinite. However, if we write the Euclidean distance formula in terms of homogeneous coordinates, the distance between two points $A(a_1, a_2, a_3)$ and $B(b_1, b_2, b_3)$ becomes

$$\frac{\sqrt{(b_1a_3 - b_3a_1)^2 + (b_2a_3 - b_3a_2)^2}}{a_3b_3}.$$

From this we see that the distance from a real point of the Euclidean plane to the point I or J is indeterminate.

We must point out here that the Euclidean distance formula does not satisfy the metric space axioms (Sec. 6.6) when it is used for imaginary points. For example, the distance from $A(0, 0, 1)$ to $B(i, 1, 1)$ is zero even though $A \neq B$. We shall, however, continue to use the word "distance" when referring to the result of applying the above formula to *any* two points.

THEOREM 7.17   *The locus of points at zero "distance" from a given real point consists of the two complex lines joining the given point to the two circular points at infinity, $I(i, 1, 0)$ and $J(-i, 1, 0)$.*

Let the given point be $A(a_1, a_2, a_3)$. Then the above formula gives the equation of the required locus as

$$(x_1a_3 - x_3a_1)^2 + (x_2a_3 - x_3a_2)^2 = 0.$$

This consists of the two lines

$$(x_1a_3 - x_3a_1) + i(x_2a_3 - x_3a_2) = 0 \quad \text{and}$$

$$(x_1a_3 - x_3a_1) - i(x_2a_3 - x_3a_2) = 0.$$

The first line contains A and J, the second contains A and I.

DEFINITION 7.13 Lines through I and J are called *isotropic* lines.

THEOREM 7.18 *Under similarity transformations I and J are invariant as a pair.* (Proof left to student.)

COROLLARY 1 *Under similarity transformations circles are transformed into circles and isotropic lines into isotropic lines.*

COROLLARY 2 *Under similarity transformations the cross-ratio of any two lines and the isotropic lines through their point of intersection is invariant.*

This suggested to Laguerre a projective interpretation of the Euclidean angle between two lines, which we will now investigate. We assume the properties of Euclidean geometry and trigonometry.

THEOREM 7.19 *In the Euclidean plane, if two real lines a and b form an angle $\measuredangle(a, b)$ at their point of intersection 0, then for a suitable choice of k, the measure of the angle is given by*

$$\measuredangle(a, b) = k \ln R(a, b, OI, OJ), \text{ mod } 2k\pi i.$$

Before we prove this we note that the logarithm is used because we want $\measuredangle(a, b) + \measuredangle(b, c) = \measuredangle(a, c)$ for three concurrent lines. The sum of the cross-ratios involved in the first two angles does not equal the third, but the product does (Th. 5.33). We also want $\measuredangle(a, a) = 0$. But $R(a, a, OI, OJ) = 1$ (Def. 5.32). Therefore we use the logarithm of the cross-ratio. Since this cross-ratio will in general be a complex number we recall that for $z = x + iy = r(\cos \theta + i \sin \theta) = re^{i\theta}$, where $\theta = \tan^{-1}(y/x)$ and $r = (x^2 + y^2)^{1/2}$, we have $\ln z = \ln r + i\theta$, mod $2\pi i$. For example, $\ln(-1) = \ln e^{i\pi} = i\pi$, mod $2\pi i$.

Now for the proof of the theorem, let 0 be point $(0, 0, 1)$. Then any two real lines a, b through 0 have equations $y = m_1x$ and $y = m_2x$ or real homogeneous coordinates $[m_1, -1, 0]$ and $[m_2, -1, 0]$, respectively. Line OI has coordinates $[1, -i, 0]$ and OJ has coordinates $[1, i, 0]$.

Therefore $R(a, b, OI, OJ) = \dfrac{\begin{vmatrix} 1 & -i \\ m_1 & -1 \end{vmatrix} \cdot \begin{vmatrix} 1 & i \\ m_2 & -1 \end{vmatrix}}{\begin{vmatrix} 1 & -i \\ m_2 & -1 \end{vmatrix} \cdot \begin{vmatrix} 1 & i \\ m_1 & -1 \end{vmatrix}}$

$$= \frac{(-1 + im_1)(-1 - im_2)}{(-1 + im_2)(-1 - im_1)}$$

$$= \frac{(1 + m_1m_2) + i(m_2 - m_1)}{(1 + m_1m_2) - i(m_2 - m_1)}$$

which may be written as $\dfrac{c + id}{c - id}$.

Now let $(c + id) = re^{i\theta}$ where $\theta = \tan^{-1}(d/c)$. Then

$$(c - id) = re^{-i\theta} \quad \text{and}$$

$$R(a, b, OI, OJ) = \frac{re^{i\theta}}{re^{-i\theta}} = e^{2i\theta}.$$

Therefore $k \ln R(a, b, OI, OJ) = 2ki\theta$, mod $2k\pi i$.

But $\theta = \tan^{-1}(d/c) = \tan^{-1} \dfrac{m_2 - m_1}{1 + m_1m_2}$.

This identifies θ with the directed Euclidean angle from a to b. We wish then to choose k so that $\measuredangle(a, b)$ as given in the theorem shall equal θ; i.e., so that $2ki\theta = \theta$. Hence $k = -i/2$ and Laguerre's theorem states that the measure of $\measuredangle(a, b)$ is given by

$$\measuredangle(a, b) = -i/2 \ln R(a, b, OI, OJ), \text{ mod } \pi.$$

[Note that $\measuredangle(a, b)$ represents a directed angle and may be obtuse.]

COROLLARY   *Two real lines in the Euclidean plane are perpendicular if and only if they are harmonic conjugates with respect to the isotropic lines through their point of intersection.*

Exercises

1. Find the line joining points $(1, i, 1 + i)$ and $(1, -i, 1 - i)$.
2. Find the point of intersection of lines $[2, -i, 1 + i]$ and $[2i, -1, 1 + i]$.
3. Prove Theorem 7.11.
4. Prove Theorem 7.12.
5. Prove Theorem 7.13.
6. Show that the lines of Ex. 2 are conjugate complex lines.
7. Find the real point on the line $[2, i, 2 - 3i]$.
8. Find the real line through the point $(1, 1 + i, 1 - i)$.
9. Prove Theorem 7.14.
10. Find the points on the line $x_1 + 2x_2 - x_3 = 0$, which are at zero distance from $(0, 0, 1)$.

11. Prove Theorem 7.18 and its corollaries.

12. Prove the corollary to Theorem 7.19.

13. Show that the Euclidean angle between two parallel lines is zero.

14. Show that the lines joining a real point to two conjugate imaginary points are conjugate imaginary lines.

7.2   A Metric for the Projective Plane

In his paper of 1858, *Sixth Memoir upon Quantics*, Arthur Cayley introduced a metric into the projective plane based on a given conic called the *absolute*, and considered the projective transformations that leave this conic invariant. By taking the absolute as an imaginary conic he obtained a system of spherical geometry (the elliptic geometry of Chapter 1); by taking the absolute as a degenerate conic in the form of a given line counted twice he obtained Euclidean geometry. Since these were the only metric geometries then known to him he stopped there, declaring that projective geometry is *all* geometry. It remained for Felix Klein, in 1871, to include hyperbolic geometry by taking the absolute as a real conic. Klein also saw the fundamental importance of Laguerre's formula, incorporated it into Cayley's work and brought the non-Euclidean geometries into his *Erlanger Programm*. We will now indicate how this was done.

We consider only conics determined by polarities with real coefficients (Sec. 5.6).

DEFINITION 7.21   Let a given hyperbolic polarity determine a *real* conic called the *absolute conic*. Then the geometry associated with the set of points in the real projective plane which are interior to the absolute conic and the group of collineations which leave the conic and its interior invariant, is called *hyperbolic plane geometry*.

DEFINITION 7.22   Let a given elliptic polarity determine an *imaginary conic* called the *absolute conic*. Then the geometry associated with the set of points in the real projective plane and the group of collineations which leave the conic invariant is called *elliptic plane geometry*.

We shall show how Laguerre's projective formula for the Euclidean angle can be generalized to the hyperbolic and elliptic geometries and dualized to give definitions of the distance between two points.

By proper choice of coordinate system a real non-degenerate conic can be expressed in the form $x_1^2 + x_2^2 - x_3^2 = 0$, an imaginary one in the form $x_1^2 + x_2^2 + x_3^2 = 0$ (Def. 5.69 and Cor. to Th. 5.69). The degenerate conic representing the ideal line counted twice is given by $x_3^2 = 0$. All three may be expressed by the equation $c(x_1^2 + x_2^2) + x_3^2 = 0$, where $c = -1, +1$, or 0, respectively. The equation of the corresponding line conic would then be $u_1^2 + u_2^2 + cu_3^2 = 0$.

When $c = 0$ the line conic becomes $u_1^2 + u_2^2 = 0$, or, in factored form $(u_1 + iu_2)(u_1 - iu_2) = 0$. Hence the degenerate line conic consists of the two pencils of lines through points $I(i, 1, 0)$ and $J(-i, 1, 0)$, namely, the isotropic lines of Section 7.1. Thus in Laguerre's projective definition of Euclidean angle, the lines OI and OJ may be considered as tangents to the point conic $x_3^2 = 0$. We are now ready to extend these ideas to obtain the general projective measure of the angle between two lines a and b.

DEFINITION 7.23   Consider an arbitrary conic as the absolute. Then the *measure of* $\measuredangle (a, b)$ is defined as $k \ln R(a, b, p, q)$, where p and q are the two tangents to the absolute conic from point $a \cdot b$, and where k depends on the unit of measurement. Dually, we define the *distance* between two points A and B as $d(AB) = k' \ln R(A, B, P, Q)$, where P and Q are the points of intersection of line AB with the point conic.

If line AB is tangent to the absolute conic then P and Q coincide. Then $R(A, B, P, Q) = 1$ (Def. 5.32), and $d(AB) = 0$, for all points A and B on the line. The line is then called an *isotropic line*. Dually, the angle between two lines which intersect in a point on the absolute conic has measure zero. Distance in the projective plane is not an inherent property of two points, but a property of these points relative to an absolute conic, which may be chosen arbitrarily. Thus isotropic lines are not special in themselves; they are so because of a particular choice of the absolute conic.

To summarize: We take the absolute conic as

$$c(x_1^2 + x_2^2) + x_3^2 = 0$$

and study the properties invariant under the subgroup of the group of real collineations that keep this conic invariant.

For *hyperbolic geometry* we let $c = -1$. The absolute conic is real and non-degenerate. We define points of the hyperbolic plane, which we shall call *h-points*, as the set of points of the real projective plane which are interior to the absolute conic; and *h-lines* as open chords of the conic.

For *elliptic geometry* we take $c = 1$. The absolute conic is an imaginary conic. We define points of the elliptic plane, *e-points*, as the set of points in the real projective plane which are not on the absolute conic; i.e., all the points of the real projective plane are *e*-points. Similarly, all the lines of the real projective plane are *e*-lines.

For *Euclidean geometry* (sometimes called *parabolic geometry*) we take $c = 0$. The absolute conic degenerates to the line $x_3 = 0$ taken twice. I and J are called the *absolute points*. We define points of the parabolic plane as the set of points of the real projective plane which are not on the absolute conic; i.e., the points of the real affine plane. Lines of the parabolic plane are lines of the real projective plane which do not go through I and J; i.e., all real projective lines except the line $x_3 = 0$.

The names *hyperbolic, elliptic,* and *parabolic* are due to Klein and come from the fact that a line in each of these planes meets its absolute conic in two real points, two imaginary points, and two coincident points, respectively (cf. Def. 6.31).

We now proceed to some details of the two non-Euclidean geometries. The existence of collineations which keep a given conic invariant is assured by the fact that a harmonic homology (Def. 5.54), whose center and axis are pole and polar with respect to a conic, keeps that conic invariant (Sec. 5.6, Ex. 16).

7.3　A Projective Model of the Real Hyperbolic Plane

The points (*h*-points) and lines (*h*-lines) of the hyperbolic plane were defined in Section 7.2. In this section we shall introduce further definitions and indicate some elementary consequences of them.

Definition 7.31　Two *h*-lines are *parallel* if they are parts of projective lines which intersect on the absolute conic. Two *h*-lines are *ultra-parallel* if they are parts of projective lines which intersect outside the absolute conic. Two *h*-lines are *perpendicular* if they are parts of projective lines which are conjugate with respect to the conic (dual of Def. 5.63).

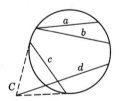

Fig. 7.31

These are illustrated in Fig. 7.31 where $a \parallel b$, b and c are ultra-parallel, and c and d are perpendicular.

The following theorems are left to the student to prove:

Theorem 7.31　*Any two distinct h-points determine a unique h-line.*

Theorem 7.32　*Any two distinct h-lines determine at most one h-point.*

Theorem 7.33　*Through a given h-point P not on a given h-line m, there are exactly two h-lines parallel to m.*

Theorem 7.34　*Through a given h-point there is exactly one h-line perpendicular to a given h-line.*

THEOREM 7.35   *Two h-lines which are perpendicular to the same h-line are ultra-parallel.*

COROLLARY   *If an h-line is perpendicular to one of two parallel h-lines, it cannot be perpendicular to the other.*

THEOREM 7.36   *Two ultra-parallel h-lines have a unique common perpendicular.*

Angle measure in the hyperbolic plane: We recall that the measure of the angle between two lines has been defined as $k \ln R(a, b, p, q)$, where p and q are the tangents to the absolute conic from the point $a \cdot b$ and where k depends on the unit of measure. If $a \parallel b$ then $a \cdot b$ is on the conic, the tangents p and q coincide, the cross-ratio is 1 and its logarithm is zero. Therefore the angle between two parallel lines has measure zero. If a is perpendicular to b and we wish a right angle to have the measure $\pi/2$, we choose k so that the measure of $\sphericalangle(a, b) = \pi/2$ when a goes through the pole of b; i.e., when a, b and p, q are harmonically separated. In this case the cross-ratio is -1 and $\ln R(a, b, p, q) = \pi i$. We therefore choose k so that $k\pi i = \pi/2$. Then $k = -i/2$ and the measure of $\sphericalangle(a, b) = -i/2 \ln R(a, b, p, q)$ as it was for Laguerre's formula for Euclidean angle. To assure the reader that the measure of $\sphericalangle(a, b)$ will also be real for other angles we note the following: The tangents p and q to the absolute conic from an h-point S are the lines which join S to the points of intersection of the conic with the polar of S (Th. 5.66). The polar of a point inside the conic does not intersect the conic in real points (Def. 5.67), but in two conjugate imaginary points (roots of a quadratic equation with real coefficients). The required tangents are lines joining a real point to each of two conjugate imaginary points and are therefore conjugate imaginary lines. Hence $R(a, b, p, q)$ is the ratio of two conjugate complex numbers and $\ln R(a, b, p, q)$ is pure imaginary (see proof of Th. 7.19). Thus multiplication by another pure imaginary number, $-i/2$ makes the measure of $\sphericalangle(a, b)$ real.

Distance in the hyperbolic plane: Let A and B be two h-points and let the projective line determined by them intersect the absolute conic in points P and Q. Then consider the expression $d(AB) = k' \ln R(A, B, P, Q)$. Since points A, B and P, Q do not separate each other the cross-ratio is positive, its logarithm is real, and we may choose k' as a real positive number. If we fix the order of P and Q in the cross-ratio we set up a direction on the line; i.e., $d(AB) = -d(BA)$ and if C is any h-point on line AB we have $d(AB) + d(BC) = d(AC)$. Therefore if we wish $d(AB) > 0$ and $d(AB) = d(BA)$ we define the *distance* between two points as $d(AB) = k' |\ln R(A, B, P, Q)|$. It can be shown that $d(AB) = 0$ if and only if $A = B$ and that the triangle inequality holds for this definition of distance. We shall refer to the expression $k' \ln R(A, B, P, Q)$ as the *directed distance AB*.

THEOREM 7.37   *If we are given h-points A and B on h-line m and an h-point A' on h-line m', there exists a unique h-point B' on m' such that directed distance A'B' is equal to directed distance AB.*

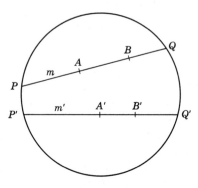

FIG. 7.32

Let P and Q be the points of intersection of the absolute conic with the projective line of which m is a part; let P' and Q' be the points of intersection of the conic with the projective line of which m' is a part (Fig. 7.32). By Theorem 5.36 a unique point B' exists on line $P'Q'$ such that $R(A', B', P', Q') = R(A, B, P, Q)$. B' is inside the conic, and therefore on h-line m'; for, if it were not, then $A'B'$ // $P'Q'$ and $R(A', B', P', Q') < 0$ while $R(A, B, P, Q) > 0$. Note that if we let B approach Q then $R(A, B, P, Q)$ approaches zero and $d(AB)$ becomes infinitely large.

THEOREM 7.38   *A harmonic homology (Def. 5.54) whose center and axis are pole and polar with respect to the absolute conic is an isometry, or rigid motion, of the hyperbolic plane.*

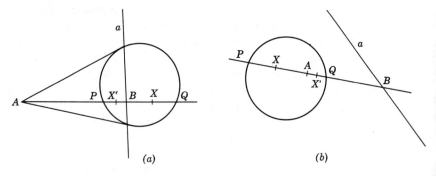

(a)   (b)

FIG. 7.33

To prove this we must show that the homology keeps the conic invariant and that the transform of an interior point is also an interior point. The theorem will then follow since cross-ratio is invariant under any collineation. Let A and a be the center and axis of a harmonic homology, and let a be the polar of A with respect to the absolute conic (Fig. 7.33). Let X be any h-point and let the projective line AX intersect the conic in P and Q. Let $AX \cdot a = B$. By the corollary to Theorem 5.67 we have $H(A, B, P, Q)$. But under the harmonic homology A and B are fixed points and hence P and Q are interchanged. Therefore the conic is invariant. Now if X' is the point corresponding to X under the homology, then $R(P, Q, B, X) = R(Q, P, B, X')$. Therefore X and X' are on the same segment determined by P and Q; i.e., on the segment containing B if the cross-ratio is positive [Fig. 7.33(a), where A is outside the conic] or on the segment not containing B if the cross-ratio is negative [Fig. 7.33(b), where A is inside the conic]. Note that, in the first case [Fig. 7.33(a)], directed distance BX is the negative of directed distance BX' and that the axis a contains an h-line perpendicular to h-line XX'. Hence this homology is called a *reflection in line a*. In the second case [Fig. 7.33(b)] directed distance AX is the negative of directed distance AX' and the homology is called a *reflection in point A*. It can be shown that all the rigid motions of the hyperbolic plane are the harmonic homologies of Theorem 7.38 or products of such homologies (see Levy, Chap. V).

On the basis of the above definitions and theorems we can develop hyperbolic geometry and see that this is indeed isomorphic to the hyperbolic geometry of Chapter 1. This is, however, beyond the scope of this book. The interested reader is referred to the books listed at the end of this chapter.

Exercises

1. Prove Theorems 7.13 through 7.36.

2. Illustrate the following h-lines: Given $a \parallel b$ (a) draw c parallel to a but not parallel to b; (b) draw d intersecting a but ultra-parallel to b; (c) draw e parallel to a and perpendicular to b.

3(a). Draw an h-line parallel to both of two given intersecting h-lines. How many such h-lines are possible? Explain. (b) Draw an h-line parallel to both of two given parallel h-lines. How many such h-lines are possible? Explain. (c) Draw an h-line parallel to both of two given ultra-parallel h-lines. How many such lines are possible? Explain.

4. Given an h-angle $\sphericalangle(a, b)$. Show that there are points P within the angle such that *no* h-line through P intersects *both* sides of the angle in h-points.

5. An *asymptotic* triangle (Sec. 1.4) may be defined as a triangle which has one vertex on the absolute conic and the other two vertices inside the conic. Show that for any asymptotic triangle $AB\Omega$ there is a unique h-line parallel to $A\Omega$ and $B\Omega$ and perpendicular to AB.

6. Show that two h-lines are ultra-parallel if and only if they have a common perpendicular.

7. Show that Exercise 20 of Section 5.6 can be used to prove that the altitudes of a triangle in the hyperbolic plane are concurrent at a point in the projective plane. However, their point of intersection is not necessarily an h-point. Draw diagrams to illustrate the following: The altitudes of a triangle in the hyperbolic plane may intersect in an h-point, or they may be parallel, or they may be ultra-parallel.

8. Show that in the real hyperbolic plane (a) $d(AB) = 0$ if and only if $A = B$; (b) directed distance AB is the negative of directed distance BA; (c) for three collinear points A, B, C, the sum of the directed distances AB and BC is equal to the directed distance AC.

9. Given the absolute conic $x_1{}^2 + x_2{}^2 - x_3{}^2 = 0$ and h-points $A(0, 0, 1)$, $B(1, 0, 2)$, $C(4, 0, 5)$, show that B is the midpoint of AC; i.e., show that directed distance AB is equal to the directed distance BC.

10. In non-homogeneous coordinates the absolute conic of Exercise 9 has the equation $x^2 + y^2 = 1$. Let A be the h-point on line $y = 0$, whose non-homogeneous parameter is 0; let B be any h-point on line $y = 0$, whose non-homogeneous parameter is x; and let d be the directed distance AB using P and Q as points with non-homogeneous parameters 1 and -1, respectively. Show that for a suitable choice of k, $x = \tanh d$.

(*Note:* This says that the Euclidean distance AB is the hyperbolic tangent of the hyperbolic distance AB.)

7.4   A Projective Model of the Real Elliptic Plane

The points (e-points) and lines (e-lines) of the real elliptic plane were defined in Section 7.2 as those of the real projective plane. The absolute conic is taken as the imaginary conic $x_1{}^2 + x_2{}^2 + x_3{}^2 = 0$. Every real point, however, has a real polar so that the polar of every e-point is an e-line and dually, the pole of every e-line is an e-point.

DEFINITION 7.41   Two e-lines are *perpendicular* if they are conjugate with respect to the absolute conic; i.e., if each goes through the pole of the other.

The following theorems are immediate consequences of the definitions:

THEOREM 7.41   *Two e-points determine a unique e-line.*

THEOREM 7.42   *Two e-lines determine a unique e-point.*

THEOREM 7.43   *All the lines perpendicular to a given e-line are concurrent at an e-point.*

Distance and angle in the elliptic plane: Considerations similar to those of Section 7.3 for angle in the hyperbolic plane show that the formula for angle measure is the same in the hyperbolic, elliptic, and Euclidean planes. The case for the distance between two e-points is, however, quite different from that of distance between two h-points. Since P and Q, the points of intersection of line AB with the absolute conic, are now conjugate imaginary points, the situation resembles that of $\angle(a, b)$. The arbitrary constant involved in the distance formula must be pure imaginary if we want distance to be real. Therefore we take $d(AB) = -ki/2 \ln R(A, B, P, Q)$, where k is real and positive and depends on the unit of length chosen.

THEOREM 7.44   *The distance from an e-point to any point on its polar is $k\pi/2$.*

From the discussion of angle in the hyperbolic plane it is seen that the distance between two points harmonically separated by P and Q is $k\pi/2$. But this is the case when two points are so situated that one is on the polar of the other.

THEOREM 7.45   *The length of a line is finite and equal to $k\pi$.*

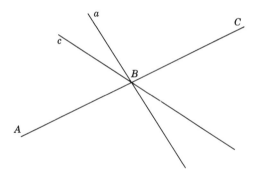

FIG. 7.41

Let e-point B be on the polar a of e-point A (Fig. 7.41). Then $d(AB) = k\pi/2$. If we continue on line AB to a point C whose distance from A is $k\pi$, then C is the pole of a line c through B. If $c \neq a$ then, since B is on a and c, B must be the pole of line AC. Hence B is on its own polar and therefore on the absolute conic. But B is real and cannot be on an imaginary conic. Therefore $c = a$, point $C = A$, and the line is closed and of length $k\pi$. For this reason we impose the condition that $0 \leqq d(AB) < k\pi$.

    It is not our intention to develop the properties of elliptic geometry. We merely wished to show some similarity to the single elliptic geometry mentioned in Chapter 1, to which it can indeed be shown to be isomorphic.

    This book started with an introductory chapter on non-Euclidean geometry as a short prologue to the material on axiomatics. We have now come back again to a brief discussion of non-Euclidean geometry as a short epilogue to the material on linear transformations.

Exercises

1. Prove Theorem 7.41.
2. Prove Theorem 7.42.
3. Prove Theorem 7.43.
4. Given the absolute conic $x_1^2 + x_2^2 + x_3^2 = 0$ and points $A(0, 0, 1)$ and $B(1, 0, 0)$, find $d(AB)$.

References

Adler, Sec. 10.10–10.16, Chaps. 14 and 15; Eves, Vol. II, Sec. 10.3; Faulkner, Chap. VI; Graustein, Chap. VIII; Levy, Chap. V; Meserve, Chap. 8; Struik, Chap. 7; Woods, Chap. VII; Young (2), Secs. 72 and 73.

CHAPTER 8

CIRCULAR TRANSFORMATIONS:
INVERSION GEOMETRY

The basic transformation of our present chapter is inversion, a transformation in which circles play a major role rather than lines. Though some of the concepts of this transformation seem to have been known as early as the 16th century, the beginning of the study of inversion geometry is generally placed at 1831 with the work of L. J. Magnus.

We start with an extension of the Euclidean plane and assume an elementary knowledge of Euclidean geometry and complex numbers. We investigate the geometry associated with a group of circular transformations and show it to be analytically identical with the geometry of the complex projective line. We end by returning once again to the non-Euclidean geometries of Chapter 1 by means of circular models and show their relationship to the projective models of Chapter 7.

8.1 Inversion in a Circle: The Real Inversion Plane

DEFINITION 8.11   Let α be a circle in the Euclidean plane with center O and radius r. Then if P is any point in the plane other than O, the transformation T under which $T(P) = P'$ such that P' is on ray OP and $\overline{OP} \cdot \overline{OP'} = r^2$, is called *inversion in circle* α. O is called the *center of inversion*, α the *circle of inversion*, and r the *radius of inversion*. P and P' are called *inverse points with respect to* α.

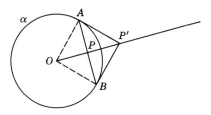

FIG. 8.11

To construct the inverse of a point P inside α we proceed as follows: Erect chord AB through P perpendicular to line OP. Construct a tangent to α at A or B (Fig. 8.11). Its intersection with line OP is P', the inverse of P. This is evident from the similar triangles OAP' and OPA. To the student is left the construction of the inverse of P if P is outside α.

Note that as P approaches O, the tangents at A and B approach parallelism. Hence the inverse of O is a point on l_∞ (Sec. 6.2), and O has no inverse in the Euclidean plane. Also if Q is a point not on line OP and if Q approaches O along line OQ, then the inverse of O is *another* point on l_∞. Therefore, in order to make inversion a one-to-one transformation we agree to consider l_∞ as a single element (or, as some prefer, we agree to add to the Euclidean plane *one* point at infinity) which is to be the inverse of O and which is to lie on *every* line of the plane. Hence the following definition:

DEFINITION 8.12   The set of points in a real Euclidean plane, together with l_∞ regarded as a single point P_∞, is called a *real inversion plane*. Two non-parallel lines will have two points in common in the real inversion plane; namely, P_∞ and their ordinary point of intersection in the Euclidean plane. Two parallel lines will be considered as being *tangent at P_∞*.

The first three theorems follow immediately from the definitions.

THEOREM 8.11   *An inversion is its own inverse and hence is an involution.*

THEOREM 8.12   *If two distinct points are inverse with respect to a circle α, then one is inside α and one is outside α.*

THEOREM 8.13   *All points on the circle of inversion are invariant points, and all lines through the center of inversion are invariant lines.*

THEOREM 8.14   *If a rectangular coordinate system is set up so that α is the circle $x^2 + y^2 = r^2$, then $P(x, y)$ and $P'(x', y')$ are inverse points with respect to α if and only if*

$$x' = \frac{r^2 x}{x^2 + y^2}, \qquad y' = \frac{r^2 y}{x^2 + y^2}.$$

If we are given the equations above, it follows that $y/x = y'/x'$ making O, P, P' collinear; and $(x^2 + y^2)^{1/2}(x'^2 + y'^2)^{1/2} = r^2$, making $OP \cdot OP' = r^2$. Hence we have the first part of the theorem. Reversing the steps and eliminating first x' and then y' from the last two equations yields the second part of the theorem.

It is of interest to note here that if we express the equations of the inversion in homogeneous coordinates (Sec. 3.10)

$$x_1' = r^2 x_1 x_3, \quad x_2' = r^2 x_2 x_3, \quad x_3' = x_1^2 + x_2^2$$

we see that *any* point on $l_\infty(x_3 = 0)$ has $(0, 0, 1)$, the center of inversion, as its inverse point.

THEOREM 8.15   *The inverse of a circle not through the center of inversion is a circle not through the center of inversion; the inverse of a circle through the center of inversion is a line not through the center of inversion.*

Consider the circle $x^2 + y^2 + 2Dx + 2Ey + F = 0$ and let α be $x^2 + y^2 = r^2$. Then the inverse of the given circle is

$$r^4 + 2Dr^2x' + 2Er^2y' + F(x'^2 + y'^2) = 0.$$

This is a circle if $F \neq 0$ (i.e., if the given circle did not go through O), and a line if $F = 0$. In either case the transform does not go through O, since $r \neq 0$.

COROLLARY 1   *The inverse of a line not through the center of inversion is a circle through the center of inversion.*

COROLLARY 2   *The inverse of a circle β through the center of inversion O is a line parallel to the tangent to β at O.*

Since it will be convenient to say that under inversion circles are transformed into circles, we make the following definitions:

DEFINITION 8.13   By a *"circle" of the inversion plane* we shall mean either a Euclidean circle, or a Euclidean line to which P_∞ has been added.

DEFINITION 8.14   An *inversion in a "circle" of the inversion plane* is either the transformation of Definition 8.11 or, if the "circle" is a Euclidean line plus P_∞, an orthogonal reflection in that line. In the latter case, all points on the line are invariant points, and all lines perpendicular to the given line are invariant lines.

In proving theorems in the inversion plane we shall use many Euclidean theorems. Hence most theorems will require proofs under different cases depending on whether the "circles" involved are ordinary Euclidean circles or Euclidean lines plus P_∞, and whether any of the points involved are ordinary Euclidean points or P_∞. For example, the following Theorem 8.16 and its corollary should be proven for the following cases: (1) α and β both Euclidean circles; (2) α a Euclidean circle, β a line; (3) α a line, β a Euclidean circle; (4) α and β lines; (5) P and P' both ordinary points, α a Euclidean circle; (6) P and P' both ordinary points, α a line; (7) $P = P_\infty$, α a Euclidean circle.

In most cases we shall present only one case and leave the others to the student.

THEOREM 8.16   *A "circle" β orthogonal to the "circle" of inversion α, is invariant under the inversion; and conversely, a "circle," other than α, which is invariant under the inversion in α, is orthogonal to α. Moreover, if β is a Euclidean circle, the set of points interior to β is also invariant.*

If α is a Euclidean circle, then Theorem 8.13 covers the case where β is a Euclidean line plus P_∞. The proof for the case where β is also a Euclidean circle follows: Let P be a point of intersection of orthogonal circles α and β.

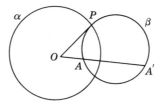

FIG. 8.12

Then OP is tangent to β (Fig. 8.12). If A is any point on β and if OA intersects β again in A', then $(OP)^2 = OA \cdot OA'$ (Euclid III 36), making A' and A inverse points with respect to α. The proof of the converse and the rest of the theorem is left to the student.

COROLLARY   *Two distinct points P and P' are inverse with respect to a given "circle" α if and only if every "circle" through P and P' is orthogonal to α.*

THEOREM 8.17   *The measure of the angle of intersection of two "circles," β and μ, in the inversion plane, is invariant under inversion in α.*

If β and μ intersect at the center of inversion O, they invert into two lines each parallel to the tangent to its corresponding circle at O (Cor. 2 of Th. 8.15) and the theorem follows. If β and μ intersect at $P \neq O$, they invert into two circles β' and μ' intersecting at P', the inverse of P (Fig. 8.13). The tangent lines m and n to β and μ at P invert into two circles m' and n' through O which meet again at P', and which have tangents at O parallel to m and n, respectively. Therefore, the angle between lines m and n is congruent to the angle between m' and n'. But since m is tangent to β at P, P is their only point of intersection. Hence m' is tangent to β' at P'. Similarly, n' is tangent to μ' at P'. Therefore the angle between β' and μ' is congruent

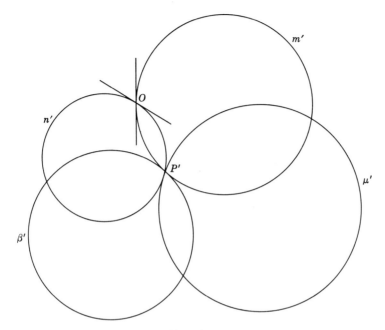

FIG. 8.13

to the angle between m' and n', which is congruent to the angle between m and n and hence to the angle between β and μ.

Note that though the measure of the angle between two "circles" is invariant under inversion, the direction of the angle is reversed. This can be seen by considering the angle between line m through O, and circles β and β', the inverse of β with respect to α (Fig. 8.14). As a point moves from P in the

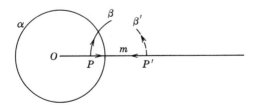

FIG. 8.14

direction of the arrows, its inverse moves from P' in the direction of the arrows. Thus the angle from m to β is opposite in direction to the angle from m' $(=m)$ to β'.

Definition 8.15　A transformation which preserves angle measure is called a *conformal transformation*.

We have shown that inversion is conformal in the special case of angles between "circles" of the inversion plane. This is sufficient for our purposes. For the general proof of conformality, the student is referred to the books listed at the end of this chapter; e.g., Graustein, P. 366.

Theorem 8.18　*If A and B are inverse points with respect to "circle" α, and if A', B', α' are inverses of A, B, α, respectively, with respect to "circle" μ, then A' and B' are inverse points with respect to α'; i.e., the inverse relationship between two points is invariant under inversion.*

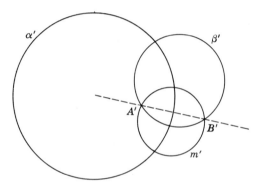

Fig. 8.15

Since A and B are inverse points with respect to "circle" α, any "circle" β through A and B is orthogonal to α. Under the inversion with respect to μ, β' is a "circle" through A' and B' orthogonal to α' (Fig. 8.15); and the inverse of line m through A and B is a circle m' through A' and B' orthogonal to α'. Therefore β' and m' are invariant under inversion with respect to α', and hence A' and B' must be inverse points with respect to α'. The student should show that this proof is still valid when any of the inversions are orthogonal line reflections.

Corollary　*If A and B are inverse points with respect to α and if B' and α' are the inverses of B and α with respect to any inversion whose center is A, then B' is the center of α'.*

Exercises

1. Show how to construct the inverse of a point P outside the circle of inversion.
2. Prove theorems 8.11, 8.12, 8.13.
3. Under inversion what happens to (a) a pencil of Euclidean parallel lines,

(b) a pencil of Euclidean concurrent lines, (c) a circle concentric to the circle of inversion, (d) the Euclidean distance between two points. Prove your answers.

4. Show that the following definition of inversion is equivalent to Definition 8.11: Point P' is the inverse of point P with respect to a circle α with center O, if P' is the point of intersection of line OP with the polar of P with respect to α.

5. Prove the corollaries to Theorems 8.15 and 8.18.

6. Complete the proof of Theorem 8.16 and its corollary.

7. Show that Theorems 8.16, 8.17, and 8.18 hold when the inversions involved are orthogonal line reflections.

8. Investigate the following and prove your conclusion: Is the inverse of the center of a given circle the center of the inverse of the given circle?

9. Given two concentric circles, prove that the system of concentric circles obtained from these by repeated inversion in each of the circles of the system, have radii in geometric progression.

10. Given a Euclidean circle α and a point A outside α, $(A \neq P_\infty)$, show that there exists a circle with center A with respect to which α may be inverted into itself. What is the corresponding theorem if $A = P_\infty$? What is the corresponding theorem if α is a line?

11. Given a "circle" α and a point A not on α, show that there exists a "circle" with respect to which α and A are inverted into a circle and its center.

12. Show that if two Euclidean circles intersect orthogonally, the inverse of the center of the first with respect to the second coincides with the inverse of the center of the second with respect to the first.

13. Show that the product of the inversions in two concentric circles with radii r_1 and r_2 is a dilation (Def. 6.52) which multiplies Euclidean distances by $(r_2/r_1)^2$.

14. Show that if P and P' are inverse points with respect to a "circle" α then the ratio of the distances to P and P' from any point A on α is independent of A. If α is a Euclidean circle with center O, show that $(AP/AP')^2 = OP/OP'$.

15. Given a Euclidean circle α and a point A not on α, show that if A is used as the center of an inversion, then the inverse of any point B inside α is a point B' such that (a) B' is outside α' if A is inside α and (b) B' is inside α' if A is outside α. State and prove the corresponding theorem if B is a point outside α.

8.2 Applications of Inversion

In this section we show how the transformation of inversion may be used to prove certain theorems in the Euclidean plane as well as the inversion plane. The method of proof consists of using a suitable center of inversion to transform the given theorem to a simpler one, proving the simpler one and inverting back to the original theorem. We choose as illustrations theorems which we shall use later. The method applies only to theorems involving properties which are invariant under inversion. The student should investigate all special cases of the theorems (cf. note after Def. 8.14).

THEOREM 8.21 *Through two given points one and only one "circle" can in general be drawn orthogonal to a given "circle."*

Let the given "circle" and points be α, A, B (Fig. 8.21, where, for the sake of simplicity, the given parts and their inverses are drawn as separate dia-

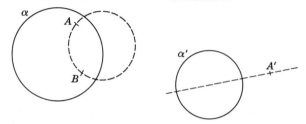

FIG. 8.21

grams). Use one of the points, B, as center of inversion. Then the inverses of α, A, B are α', A', P_∞, respectively. The transformed problem requires a line through A' orthogonal to α'. This is the line joining A' to the center of α'. We invert back and have the original theorem. Note that the required "circle" is not unique if A and B are inverse points with respect to α. Why?

THEOREM 8.22　　*Through a given point A, not on both of two given "circles" α and β, one and only one "circle" can be drawn orthogonal to α and β.*

Using the given point as center of inversion transforms the problem to one requiring a line orthogonal to two given circles. This is the line joining their centers.

THEOREM 8.23　　*Through a given point A, not on a given "circle" α, one and only one "circle" can be drawn tangent to α at a given point P on α.*

Using A as center of inversion transforms the problem to that of requiring a tangent to a circle at a point on it. Using P as center of inversion transforms the problem to that of requiring a line through A' parallel to α'. Each of these is a simple Euclidean problem.

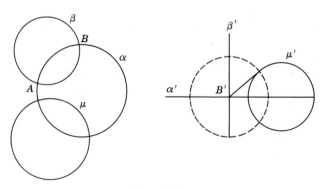

FIG. 8.22

THEOREM 8.24   *Given three "circles" α, β, μ, such that β and μ are nonintersecting and both orthogonal to α, there is a unique "circle" orthogonal to all three given "circles."*

Let α and β intersect in points A and B (Fig. 8.22) and use A as center of inversion. Then α' and β' are two perpendicular lines intersecting at B', and μ' is a circle whose center is on α'. The transformed problem requires a circle orthogonal to α', β', and μ'. Its center will therefore be B' and its radius the length of a tangent from B' to μ'.

THEOREM 8.25   *Given a "circle" α and a line m containing a given point P not on α, there is a unique "circle" orthogonal to α and tangent to m at P.*

This can be shown directly by taking P', the inverse of P with respect to α, and noting that the center of the required circle is the intersection of the line perpendicular to m at P and the line perpendicular to PP' at its midpoint (Cor. to Th. 8.16). If α is a Euclidean circle and if m goes through the center of α, then m is the required "circle."

Exercises

1. Investigate all possible cases of the theorems of this section (see note after Def. 8.14).

2. Use the transformation of inversion to transform Theorem 8.25 to a simpler one and prove it.

3. Show that through two distinct points A and B not on a given "circle" α, two and only two "circles" can in general be drawn tangent to α. What are the exceptional cases?

4. Given three "circles" with just one point in common and no two tangent to each other, show that there exist four circles each of which is tangent to all three given circles.

5. Given a Euclidean circle with center O, diameter AB, and any third point C on the circumference, prove that the circle determined by A, O, C is orthogonal to the circle determined by B, O, C.

6. Obtain new theorems by inverting the following: (a) The sum of the angles of a triangle is a straight angle. (b) An angle inscribed in a semicircle is a right angle. (c) The altitudes of a triangle are concurrent.

8.3   Coaxal "Circles"

From the corollary to Theorem 8.16 we note that if A and B are inverse points with respect to a "circle" α, the "circles" through A and B form a set of "circles" all orthogonal to α. Each "circle" of the set is transformed into itself under the inversion in α. The line AB is included in the set of "circles" through A and B.

Definition 8.31   The set of "circles" through two distinct points A and B will be called a *coaxal set of Type I*. The line AB is called the *radical axis* of the set.

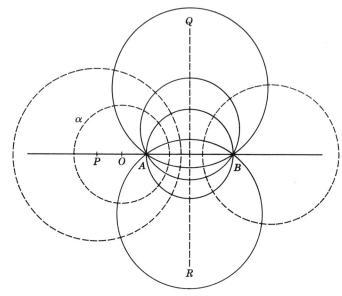

Fig. 8.31

If P is on line AB but not on segment AB (Fig. 8.31) the lengths of the tangents from P to all the circles of Set I are equal. If we denote this constant length by r, then the circle with center P and radius r is orthogonal to *all* the "circles" of Set I. By letting P take on all possible positions on line AB, outside of segment AB, we get a set of circles each orthogonal to all the "circles" of the first set. A and B are therefore inverse points with respect to each circle of the second set. The line QR, which is the perpendicular bisector of AB, is considered a "circle" of this second set since A and B are reflections of each other in line QR.

Definition 8.32   The set of "circles" with respect to which two distinct ordinary points A and B are inverse points will be called a *coaxal set of Type II*. The perpendicular bisector of segment AB is the *radical axis* of the set.

We note that the above two mutually orthogonal coaxal sets of circles have the property that the line of centers of one is the radical axis of the other.

DEFINITION 8.33   The set of "circles" tangent to each other at the same point O will be called a *coaxal set of Type III* (Fig. 8.32). Their common tangent is in the set and is called the *radical axis* of the set. The line of centers of this set is the radical axis of an orthogonal set of "circles" of the same type.

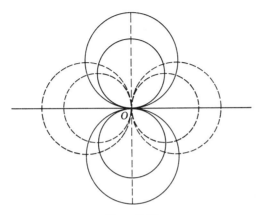

FIG. 8.32

If we invert the sets of coaxal "circles" of Types I and II (Fig. 8.31) with A as center of inversion, the set of Type I inverts into a pencil of lines through B', the inverse of B. The set of Type II, under the same inversion is transformed into a set of concentric circles with center B' (Cor. to Th. 8.18). If we invert the two sets of Type III (Fig. 8.32) with O as center of inversion, we get two sets of mutually orthogonal parallel lines. Thus we are led to the following definitions:

DEFINITIONS 8.34   A set of concurrent lines (which, we recall, are "circles" of the inversion plane) will be called a *coaxal set of Type I'*; a set of concentric circles, a *coaxal set of Type II'*; and a set of parallel lines, a *coaxal set of Type III'*.

Note that since no two circles of Set II' intersect, no two "circles" of Set II intersect.

THEOREM 8.31   *A coaxal set of "circles" is invariant as a set under inversion in any "circle" of the set.*

The theorem is obvious for sets of Types I', II', and III', and hence holds for sets of Types I, II, and III by Theorem 8.18.

THEOREM 8.32   *The points which are the inverses of a given point P with respect to all the "circles" of a given coaxal set lie on that "circle" of the orthogonal coaxal set which goes through P.*

Again the theorem is obvious for sets of Types I′, II′, III′ and hence holds for Types I, II, III.

THEOREM 8.33   *Any two "circles" in the inversion plane belong to one of the coaxal sets of Definitions 8.31–8.34.*

The theorem is obvious if the given "circles" are intersecting, or tangent, or concentric (note that this includes intersecting or parallel Euclidean lines). If the two "circles" are non-intersecting, non-concentric "circles" we shall show that there exist two points which are inverse with respect to both "circles," thus making them belong to a coaxal set of Type II. We distinguish two cases. Case 1: One "circle," α, is a Euclidean circle and the second "circle," β, is a Euclidean line plus P_∞. Let M be the foot of the perpendicular to β from the center of α (Fig. 8.33). Since M is outside α there

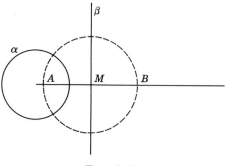

FIG. 8.33

exists a circle with M as center orthogonal to α. This intersects the line of centers in two points A and B which are inverse with respect to both α and β. Case 2: If both α and β are Euclidean circles, then inversion with any point P on β as center of inversion reduces this case to Case 1, yielding points A' and B' inverse with respect to both α' and β'. Inversion again with P as center transforms A' and B' into two points A and B which are inverse with respect to α and β.

Exercises

1. In Fig. 8.31, prove that the lengths of the tangents from any point P on AB, not on segment AB, to all circles of Set I are equal.

2. In Fig. 8.31, prove that the lengths of the tangents from any point on QR to all circle of Set II are equal.

3. Complete the proofs of Theorems 8.31 and 8.32.

4. Given any three distinct collinear points in the order O, A, B, show that there exists a unique circle with center O with respect to which A and B are inverse points.

5. Let α and β be two non-intersecting, non-concentric circles, one inside the other. Let circles be drawn tangent to both α and β and such that circle μ_1 is tangent to circle μ_2, circle μ_2 is tangent to μ_3, etc. It may happen that if we continue this process, there is a circle μ_n which is tangent to μ_1 as well as to μ_{n-1}; i.e., the ring of tangent circles is closed. Show that if this happens once it will always happen, no matter what the position of the first circle is (Steiner's Theorem).

6. Given any two "circles" α, β in the inversion plane, show that there exists a "circle" μ in the coaxal set determined by α and β, such that β is the inverse of α with respect to μ.

8.4 Circular Transformations of the Inversion Plane: The Inversion Group

DEFINITION 8.41   A transformation of the real inversion plane onto itself which transforms "circles" into "circles" is called a *circular transformation* of the inversion plane.

The inversions of Section 8.1 are circular transformations as are the similarity transformations of Chapter 6. Are there others? We shall show the following:

THEOREM 8.41   *Every circular transformation of the real inversion plane is either a similarity transformation, an inversion in a Euclidean circle, or the product of these two.*

Case 1: T is a circular transformation of the inversion plane that leaves P_∞ invariant. Then Euclidean circles are transformed into Euclidean circles and lines into lines. Thus T is a collineation which preserves circles. Since P_∞ is l_∞, considered as one element (Def. 8.12), and is left invariant, the collineation is an affine transformtion. The most general affine transformation that preserves circles is a similarity transformation (Ex. 1 at the end of this section).

Case 2: T is a circular transformation of the inversion plane that transforms P_∞ into an ordinary point O. Then T may be an inversion in a Euclidean circle with O as center. If it is not, let T_1 be an inversion with center O. Then $T_1 T$ leaves P_∞ invariant and is therefore a similarity transformation S; i.e., $T_1 T = S$. Therefore, since T_1 is an involution, $T = T_1 S$.

We note here that every similarity transformation may be expressed as a rotation, a translation, a line reflection, a dilation, or a product of these

(Chap. 6). But a rotation and a translation can each be shown to be the product of two suitably chosen line reflections (Levi, Chap. 9); and a dilation can be expressed as the product of inversions in two suitably chosen concentric circles (Ex. 13 of Sec. 8.1). Therefore, every circular transformation is the product of inversions in "circles" of the inversion plane (Def. 8.14).

The analytic treatment of circular transformations is very much simplified if the transformations are expressed in terms of a single complex variable z instead of the pair of real numbers (x, y). For this we use the familiar Argand diagram (Fig. 8.41) and replace the ordered real number pair

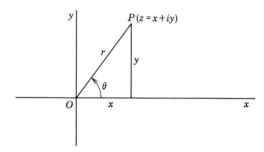

FIG. 8.41

(x, y) by the complex number $z = x + iy$, assigning to P_∞ the symbol $z = \infty$. Note that this sets up an isomorphism between the points of the inversion plane and the points of the complex projective line. We shall refer to point P as point z or point (x, y). We recall that $z = r(\cos \theta + i \sin \theta)$, where r, the *absolute value of* z, is the distance of the point (x, y) from O, and θ, the *argument of* z, is the measure of the directed angle from the positive direction of the x-axis to the directed line OP. Hence $r = |z| = (x^2 + y^2)^{1/2}$ and $|z_2 - z_1| = $ distance P_1P_2. Also $\arg(z_2 - z_1)$ is the measure of the directed angle from the positive direction of the x-axis to that of the directed segment P_1P_2. Since the argument of the quotient of two complex numbers is the difference of the arguments of the two numbers, we see that the argument of $(z_2 - z_1)/(z_2 - z_3)$ is the measure of the directed $\sphericalangle P_3P_2P_1$, mod 2π. Thus we have the following:

THEOREM 8.42   (a) *A reflection in the x-axis is given by $z' = \bar{z}$.* (b) *The inversion in the circle $|z| = r$, is given by $z' = r^2/\bar{z}$.*

Using the equations of theorem 8.14, we have

$$z' = x' + iy' = r^2(x + iy)/(x^2 + y^2) = r^2z/|z|^2.$$

But $z\bar{z} = |z|^2$, and therefore $z' = r^2/\bar{z}$.

(c) *A direct similarity transformation is given by* $z' = \alpha z + \beta$; *an indirect one by* $z' = \alpha \bar{z} + \beta$, $\alpha \neq 0$, *where* α *and* β *are complex numbers.*

This follows from the non-homogeneous equations of similarity transformations of Sec. 6.4.

COROLLARY *Inversion in the circle with center* (h, k) *and radius* r (*i.e., circle* $|z - \lambda| = r$, *where* $\lambda = h + ik$) *is given by* $z' - \lambda = r^2/(\bar{z} - \bar{\lambda})$ *or* $z' = \lambda + r^2/(\bar{z} - \bar{\lambda})$.

The following theorem is an immediate consequence of the two preceding theorems.

THEOREM 8.43 *A circular transformation of the inversion plane may be expressed as a linear fractional transformation of a complex variable of one of the following forms:*

$$z' = (\alpha z + \beta)/(\mu z + \delta), \text{ or } z' = (\alpha \bar{z} + \beta)/(\mu \bar{z} + \delta),$$

where $\alpha, \beta, \mu, \delta$ *are complex numbers and* $\alpha\delta - \beta\mu \neq 0$.

THEOREM 8.44 *Every linear fractional transformation of a complex variable is a circular transformation (converse of 8.43).*

To prove this we show that every linear fractional transformation of a complex variable is the product of similarity transformations and inversions. We do this for $z' = (\alpha z + \beta)/(\mu z + \delta)$: If $\mu = 0$, the transformation is a direct similarity transformation (Th. 8.42c). If $\mu \neq 0$, then

$$z' = \frac{\alpha z + \beta}{\mu z + \delta} = \frac{\alpha}{\mu} + \frac{\beta\mu - \alpha\delta}{\mu} \cdot \frac{1}{\mu z + \delta}.$$

This is the product of three transformations, as follows:

$$z' = \frac{\alpha}{\mu} + \frac{\beta\mu - \alpha\delta}{\mu} z_2, \quad z_2 = \frac{1}{z_1}, \quad z_1 = \mu z + \delta.$$

The first and third of these are direct similarity transformations; the second is the inversion in the circle $|z| = 1$ followed by the reflection in the x-axis (Th. 8.42a, b). All three of these are then direct circular transformations. For $z' = (\alpha \bar{z} + \beta)/(\mu \bar{z} + \delta)$, we have a similar result except for an extra reflection, $z' = \bar{z}$. Hence this is an indirect circular transformation. Note that analytically the direct circular transformations are identical with the projectivities on a complex projective line (cf. Sec. 5.2). These form a group. The indirect circular transformations do not form a group, but the two types together form the group of all circular transformations of the inversion plane. The similarity group is a subgroup of this as is therefore the group of rigid motions of the Euclidean plane.

Exercises

1. Given the affine transformation

$$x' = ax + by + c$$
$$y' = ex + fy + d,$$

show that the transform of $x'^2 + y'^2 + 2Dx' + 2Ey' + F = 0$ is of the same form if and only if $e = \pm b$ and $f = \mp a$, making the given transformation a similarity transformation.

2. By methods analogous to those used in Theorem 5.43, investigate the invariant points of a direct circular transformation.

3. What are the invariant points of the following:
(a) $z' = 1/z$, (b) $z' = 2z$, (c) $z' = (z - 1)/(z + 2)$?

4. Prove that the transformation $z' = (\alpha z + \beta)/(\mu z + \delta)$, $\alpha\delta - \mu\beta \neq 0$, is an involution if and only if $\alpha + \delta = 0$.

5. Prove that under the transformation $z' = (\alpha z + \beta)/(\mu z + \delta)$, where $\alpha\delta - \mu\beta \neq 0$ and $\mu \neq 0$, the unit circle with center at the origin ($z\bar{z} = 1$) is transformed into a straight line if and only if $|\delta| = |\mu|$.

6. Complete the proof of Theorem 8.42 and prove its corollary.

7. Prove Theorem 8.43.

8.5   Cross-Ratio in the Inversion Plane

DEFINITION 8.51   The cross-ratio of four distinct points in the inversion plane is defined as the complex number given by

$$R(P_1, P_2, P_3, P_4) = \frac{(z_3 - z_1)}{(z_3 - z_2)} \div \frac{(z_4 - z_1)}{(z_4 - z_2)}.$$

From the remarks in the last section we see that the absolute value of the cross-ratio is $|R| = (P_1P_3/P_2P_3) \div (P_1P_4/P_2P_4)$, and that the argument of the cross-ratio is

$$\arg R = \arg \frac{(z_3 - z_1)}{(z_3 - z_2)} - \arg \frac{(z_4 - z_1)}{(z_4 - z_2)}$$

$$= \text{directed } \measuredangle P_2P_3P_1 - \text{directed } \measuredangle P_2P_4P_1, \text{ mod } 2\pi$$

$$= \text{directed } \measuredangle P_2P_3P_1 + \text{directed } \measuredangle P_1P_4P_2, \text{ mod } 2\pi.$$

If one of the four points is P_∞ we may use a pair of complex homogeneous coordinates instead of the single complex number z, or we may use a limiting process. For example, if $P_4 \to P_\infty$ then $(z_4 - z_2)/(z_4 - z_1) \to 1$. We say then that

$$R(P_1, P_2, P_3, P_\infty) = (z_3 - z_1)/(z_3 - z_2), \arg R = \text{directed } \measuredangle P_2P_3P_1.$$

Note that Definition 8.51 has the same form as the non-homogeneous one for the cross-ratio of four points on a projective line (Sec. 5.3) and that theorems analogous to Theorems 5.31–5.37 can be shown to hold. However, as we noted at the end of the proof of Theorem 8.44, a projectivity on a complex line is analytically identical with a *direct* circular transformation. Hence the analog of Theorem 5.34 gives us the following:

THEOREM 8.51   *The cross-ratio of four points in the inversion plane is invariant under a direct circular transformation.*

Substitution in the equations of an indirect circular transformation shows that the following theorem holds.

THEOREM 8.52   *Under an indirect circular transformation the cross-ratio of four points is transformed into its conjugate complex number.*

THEOREM 8.53   *Four points are on a "circle" in the inversion plane if and only if their cross-ratio is real.*

The proof depends on two Euclidean theorems which we state here for convenience.

(a) Given four points A, B, C, D, no three of which are collinear, such that A and B are on the same side of CD; then a necessary and sufficient condition for A, B, C, D to be concyclic is that $\angle CAD \cong \angle CBD$ (Euclid III, 21 and its converse).

(b) Given four points A, B, C, D, no three of which are collinear, such that A and B are on opposite sides of CD; then a necessary and sufficient condition for A, B, C, D to be concyclic is that $\angle CAD$ and $\angle CBD$ be supplementary (Euclid III, 22 and converse).

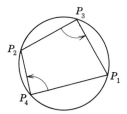 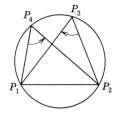

FIG. 8.51

From these it follows that if the four points P_1, P_2, P_3, P_4 are on a Euclidean circle as in Fig. 8.51 (or on a line), then the angles at P_3 and P_4 are supplementary or congruent according as the pair P_1, P_2 does or does not separate the pair P_3, P_4. Therefore

$$\arg R(P_1, P_2, P_3, P_4) = \angle P_2 P_3 P_1 + \angle P_1 P_4 P_2 = 0, \bmod \pi,$$

and the cross-ratio is real. Conversely, if R is real then arg $R = 0$, mod π, the angles at P_4 and P_3 are congruent or supplementary, and the four points are concyclic (or collinear).

Note that when P_1, P_2 and P_3, P_4 separate each other on the circle, then $R(P_1, P_2, P_3, P_4)$ is negative; when P_1, P_2 and P_3, P_4 do not separate each other, the cross-ratio is positive.

The student should show that Theorem 8.53 holds if one of the four points, say P_4, is P_∞.

COROLLARY *The cross-ratio of four points on a circle in the inversion plane is invariant under both direct and indirect circular transformations.*

THEOREM 8.54 *If a one-to-one transformation of the inversion plane preserves the cross-ratio of every set of four points, it is a direct circular transformation.*

This follows from Theorems 8.53 and 8.51.

COROLLARY *If a one-to-one transformation of the inversion plane changes the cross-ratio of every set of four points to its conjugate complex number, it is an indirect circular transformation.*

THEOREM 8.55 *There exists a unique direct (and a unique indirect) circular transformation under which three given distinct points A, B, C correspond to three given distinct points A', B', C'.*

Any fourth point D forms with A, B, C a cross-ratio k. Hence D' is uniquely determined by the equation $R(A', B', C', D') = k$ (and D_1' by the equation $R(A', B', C', D_1') = \bar{k}$). But by Theorem 8.54, the transformation determining D' is a direct circular transformation (and by its corollary, that determining D_1' is indirect).

Exercises

1. Show that under indirect circular transformations the cross-ratio of four points of the inversion plane is transformed into its conjugate complex number.

2. Show that Theorem 8.53 still holds if one of the four points is P_∞.

3. Show that $R(z, 1, 0, \infty) = z$.

4. If $R(P_1, P_2, P_3, P_4) = -1$, then show that

$$2/(z_1 - z_2) = 1/(z_1 - z_3) + 1/(z_1 - z_4).$$

5. Let three "circles" of a coaxal system of Type III (Def. 8.33) be intersected by an arbitrary orthogonal "circle" α through the point of tangency P in three points A, B, C, respectively. Prove that $R(P, A, B, C)$ is a constant for all α of the orthogonal set through P.

8.6   Inversion in a Sphere and Stereographic Projection

The concept of inversion may be easily extended to three-dimensional space.

DEFINITION 8.61   Two points P and P' in Euclidean three-space are *inverse with respect to a sphere* with center 0 and radius r if P' is on ray OP and $\overline{OP} \cdot \overline{OP'} = r^2$. To make the transformation strictly one-to-one we agree to add one point, P_∞, to Euclidean three-space to yield inversion space. P_∞ is the inverse of 0 and lies on all planes and lines.

In a manner completely analogous to the methods of Section 8.1 the following theorems may be proved:

THEOREM 8.61   *All points on the sphere of inversion are invariant points and all planes through the center of inversion are invariant planes.*

COROLLARY   *All lines through the center of inversion are invariant lines.*

THEOREM 8.62   *The inverse of a sphere not through the center of inversion is a sphere not through the center of inversion; the inverse of a sphere through the center of inversion is a plane not through the center of inversion; the inverse of a plane not through the center of inversion is a sphere through the center of inversion.*

COROLLARY   *The inverse of a circle is a circle or a line; the inverse of a line is a circle or a line. Hence if we agree as before to include lines in the general set of circles in inversion space, we can say that inversion in a sphere transforms "circles" into "circles."*

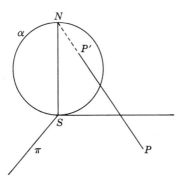

FIG. 8.61

The student should now state and prove additional theorems for inversion in a sphere which are analogous to the theorems of Section 8.1.

We now introduce a one-to-one correspondence between the points on a real Euclidean sphere and the points on a real inversion plane.

Definition 8.62   Given a Euclidean sphere α with diameter NS (Fig. 8.61), tangent to an inversion plane π at S. Then the transformation under which the point P' on the sphere, corresponding to a point P in π, is such that N, P', P are collinear, is called *stereographic projection*. Under stereographic projection N and P_∞ are corresponding points.

Theorem 8.63   *The stereographic projection of Definition 8.62 is induced by the space inversion with respect to the sphere whose center is N and whose radius is the diameter of α.*

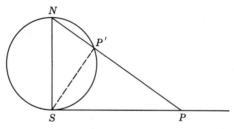

Fig. 8.62

Cut sphere α by the plane determined by NP and NS (Fig. 8.62). Then SP' is the altitude to the hypotenuse of right $\triangle NSP$. Hence $NP \cdot NP' = (NS)^2$.

The following is an immediate consequence of Definition 8.62 and Theorem 8.63.

Theorem 8.64   *Under the stereographic projection of Theorem 8.63, the "circles" of the inversion plane π correspond to circles on the Euclidean sphere α. In particular, a circle through NS on the sphere (a meridian) corresponds to a line through S on π; a circle on α in a plane perpendicular to NS (a circle of latitude) corresponds to a Euclidean circle on π with center S; a circle on α through N but not S corresponds to a line on π not through S; a circle on α not through N corresponds to a Euclidean circle on π.*

Theorem 8.65   *The measure of the angle of intersection of two "circles" in the inversion plane is unchanged under stereographic projection.*

Let P be a point of intersection of the two "circles" in the inversion plane. We consider the angle between the tangent lines m and n to the two "circles" at P (cf. proof of Th. 8.17). Under the stereographic projection these correspond to circles through N and P', whose tangents at N are respectively parallel to m and n. But these circles form congruent angles at P' and N.

Exercises

1. State and prove theorems for inversion in a sphere that are analogous to those of Section 8.1.

2. Prove Theorem 8.64.

3. Show that if a rectangular coordinate system is set up so that the equation of π in Def. 8.62 is $z = 0$, and sphere α has its center at $(0, 0, 1/2)$, and if P and P' have coordinates $(x, y, 0)$ and (x', y', z'), respectively, then the equations of the stereographic projection are:

(from P' to P): $x = \dfrac{x'}{1 - z'}, \quad y = \dfrac{y'}{1 - z'};$

(from P to P'): $x' = \dfrac{x}{x^2 + y^2 + 1}, \quad y' = \dfrac{y}{x^2 + y^2 + 1}, \quad z' = \dfrac{x^2 + y^2}{x^2 + y^2 + 1}.$

These last three equations are known as Riemann's sphere transformations, used to transform the Gauss plane of complex numbers (Argand diagram: Fig. 8.41) onto the real points on the surface of a sphere.

4. Using the equations of Ex. 3, prove analytically that, under stereographic projection, "circles" in the inversion plane correspond to circles on the sphere.

8.7 Poincaré's Circular Model of the Hyperbolic Plane

DEFINITION 8.71 Let α be a Euclidean circle in the inversion plane. Then the points of the hyperbolic plane, *h-points*, will be defined as the points of the inversion plane interior to α. The lines of the hyperbolic plane, *h-lines*, will be defined as the open arcs of "circles" of the inversion plane interior and orthogonal to α. The points on α will be called *ideal points*, and the points in which a "circle" containing an h-line intersects α will be called the ideal points of the h-line. We emphasize the fact that ideal points are *not* points of the hyperbolic plane and hence are not *on* the h-lines.

The following familiar theorems of Chapters 1 and 7 hold:

THEOREM 8.71 *Two distinct h-points determine a unique h-line.*

This follows from Theorem 8.21.

THEOREM 8.72 *Two distinct h-lines intersect in at most one h-point.*

This follows from the corollary to Theorem 8.16, and Theorem 8.12.

DEFINITION 8.72   Two *h*-lines are *parallel* if the "circles" on which they lie are tangent to each other at an ideal point; two *h*-lines are *ultra-parallel* if the "circles" on which they lie do not intersect.

DEFINITION 8.73   If two *h*-lines intersect, the *h-angle* between them is the Euclidean angle between the "circles" on which they lie. Thus two *h*-lines are perpendicular if the "circles" on which they lie are orthogonal.

THEOREM 8.73   *Through a given h-point A there is a unique h-line p perpendicular to a given h-line q and, if A is not on q, there are exactly two h-lines m and n through A parallel to q. Furthermore m and n make congruent angles with p (these are the angles of parallelism of Sec. 1.4).*

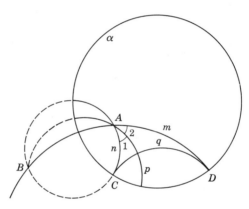

FIG. 8.71

The first two parts of the theorem follow from Theorems 8.22 and 8.23. For the last part, we must show that ∡1 and ∡2 in Fig. 8.71 are congruent. Since *m*, *n*, and *p* all go through *A* and are orthogonal to α, they all meet at a second point *B* outside α. Also since α and *q* are both orthogonal to *p*, their points of intersection *C* and *D* are inverse with respect to *p* (Cor. to Th. 8.16). Hence the inversion with respect to *p* keeps *B* and *A* fixed and interchanges *C* and *D*. Therefore this inversion keeps *p* fixed and interchanges *m* and *n*, making the angle between *n* and *p* (∡1) congruent to the angle between *m* and *p* (∡2).

DEFINITION 8.74   Let *A* and *B* be two *h*-points and let the ideal points of *h*-line *AB* be *P* and *Q*. Then the *directed h-distance AB* is given by $k \ln R(A, B, P, Q)$, where the order of *P*, *Q* is fixed in the cross-ratio for all point pairs on the h-line. The h-*length of segment* AB is given by $h(AB)$ $= k|\ln R(A, B, P, Q)|$. Two h-segments are *congruent* if their h-lengths are equal.

Note that, by Theorem 8.53, $R(A, B, P, Q)$ in Definition 8.74 is real and positive and hence its logarithm is real. We also note that as B approaches the circumference of α along h-line AB, $h(AB)$ increases without limit.

We now investigate the rigid motions of the hyperbolic plane thus defined. We shall call these h-*motions*. Since an h-motion must keep h-lengths and angle measure invariant, it must be a circular transformation which keeps α and its interior invariant. Hence the set of h-motions is the subset of the group of circular transformations which keeps α and its interior invariant. This subset forms a group and the associated geometry can be shown to be the hyperbolic geometry of Chapter 1. It can be shown that the h-motions are products of inversions which keep α and its interior invariant (cf. note after Th. 8.41). But by Theorem 8.16, these are inversions with respect to circles orthogonal to α. Therefore, the h-motions are products of inversions in the circles on which the h-lines lie. The following theorem is a fundamental one for rigid motions.

THEOREM 8.74   *There exists a unique direct (and a unique indirect) h-motion that transforms a given directed line m containing a given point A, into a given directed line m' containing a given point A'.*

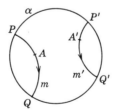

FIG. 8.72

Let the ideal points of m and m' be P, Q and P', Q', respectively, and let the directions be as indicated in Fig. 8.72. Then there is a unique direct circular transformation T_1 (and a unique indirect one T_2) that takes P, A, Q into P', A', Q', respectively (Th. 8.55). Hence $T_1(m) = m'$, and $T_1(\alpha)$ is a circle through P' and Q' orthogonal to m'; i.e., $T_1(\alpha) = \alpha$. Also since $T_1(A) = A'$ interior to α, T_1 is an h-motion. (The same holds for T_2.)

COROLLARY 1   *Given distinct h-points A, B on h-line m and an h-point A' on h-line m', there exists a unique h-point B' on m' such that directed h-distance $A'B'$ is equal to directed h-distance AB.*

COROLLARY 2   *Two h-segments are congruent if and only if there exists an h-motion which carries one onto the other.*

THEOREM 8.75   *Given two distinct non-orthogonal h-lines m, n intersecting at h-point A, and an h-line m′ containing h-point A′, there exist exactly two h-lines through A′ each of which forms with m′ an angle congruent to the angle between m and n.*

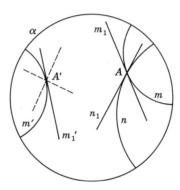

FIG. 8.73

Let m_1, n_1 be the tangent Euclidean lines at A to m, n, respectively, and let m_1' be the tangent Euclidean line at A' to m' (Fig. 8.73). Then through A' there are two Euclidean lines each making with m_1' an angle congruent to the angle between m_1 and n_1. Then Theorem 8.25 gives us the two h-lines we seek.

COROLLARY   *Two h-angles are congruent if and only if there exists an h-motion which carries one into the other.*

With the help of the above theorems, it can be shown that Hilbert's axioms for hyperbolic geometry (Appendix 2 with the Euclidean parallel postulate replaced by the hyperbolic one of Sec. 1.3) are verified in the Poincaré model (cf. Eves, p. 402–409). If this is done then the hyperbolic theorems of Chapter 1 automatically hold for the corresponding figures in the Poincaré model. We shall, however, use the Poincaré model itself to provide proofs of some of these and other theorems.

THEOREM 8.76   *The sum of the angles of an h-triangle is less than a straight angle.*

Given h-$\triangle ABC$ (Fig. 8.74). If C is not the center of α, let the "circles" on which h-lines AC and BC lie meet at R outside α. Let T be the inversion

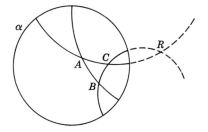 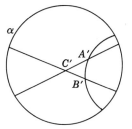

FIG. 8.74

in the circle orthogonal to α with center R. Then $T(\alpha) = \alpha$ and $T(A, B, C)$ = h-points A', B', C'. But $A'C'$ and $B'C'$ are Euclidean lines orthogonal to α. (Why?) Hence C' is the center of α. Since h-angles are Euclidean and invariant and since the sum of the angles of h-$\triangle A'B'C'$ is obviously less than a straight angle, then so is the sum of the angles of h-$\triangle ABC$.

DEFINITION 8.75 The locus of an h-point a given h-distance r from a given h-point A is called an h-circle with h-center A and h-radius r.

THEOREM 8.77 *An h-circle with center A is a Euclidean circle orthogonal to the family of h-lines through A.*

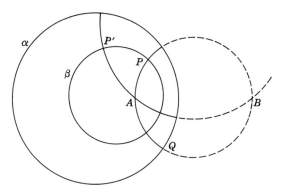

FIG. 8.75

The family of h-lines through A are on "circles" which meet again at a point B, outside α, which is inverse to A with respect to α (Fig. 8.75). They form a coaxal system of Type I. Let P be an h-point such that $h(AP) = r$. Then the inversions in circles of the family through A and B yield h-points P' such that $h(AP') = h(AP) = r$. The locus of P' is a Euclidean circle β of the orthogonal coaxal system (Th. 8.32). (What happens if A is the center of α?)

If we let h-radius AP become infinitely large by keeping P fixed and letting A move along h-line PA toward ideal point Q (Fig. 8.75) we get as the limiting form of an h-circle, a Euclidean circle internally tangent to α at Q. This is called a horocycle.

DEFINITION 8.76   A Euclidean circle internally tangent to α is called a *horocycle*.

THEOREM 8.78   *Two horocycles tangent to α at the same point Q, cut off equal h-lengths on the h-lines through Q.*

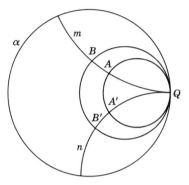

FIG. 8.76

Let m, n be any two h-lines through Q cutting the given horocycles in AB and $A'B'$, respectively (Fig. 8.76). The two horocycles (and α) belong to a coaxal system of Type III; m and n belong to the orthogonal coaxal system. Hence there is a suitable inversion in a "circle" of the second system that sends m into n. But this inversion keeps the horocycles invariant (and keeps α invariant). It thus sends A into A', and B into B', making $h(AB) = h(A'B')$.

DEFINITION 8.77   The locus of an h-point a given h-distance d from a given h-line is called an *equidistant curve* or *hypercycle* (cf. end of Sec. 1.5), of which the given h-line is the *base line*.

THEOREM 8.79   *A hypercycle whose base h-line m has ideal points P and Q consists of the arcs of two "circles" of the inversion plane through P and Q, one on each side of m and making congruent angles with m.*

Let A be any h-point on m (Fig. 8.77). On the unique h-line through A perpendicular to m, let B and C be the two h-points such that $h(AB) = h(AC) = d$, the h-length defining the hypercycle. Now m and α determine

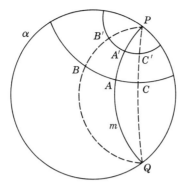

FIG. 8.77

a coaxal system of Type I through P and Q, and the perpendicular through A belongs to the orthogonal coaxal system of Type II. Then inversions in "circles" of the system of Type II (which are h-motions) yield points A', B', C', such that $h(A'B') = h(A'C') = h(AB) = d$. By Theorem 8.32, the locus of A' is m and the loci of B' and C' are arcs of "circles" through P and Q. These are *not* h-lines. As for the last part of the theorem, since $h(AB) = h(AC)$, there is an h-motion (e.g., inversion in m) transforming h-segment AB into h-segment AC (Cor. 2 to Th. 8.74). Under this h-motion circular arc PBQ will be transformed into circular arc PCQ and therefore the angles these arcs make with m are congruent. Note that as $d \to \infty$, the angle between the hypercycle and its base line approaches $\pi/2$ and the hypercycle approaches α.

COROLLARY 1   *The h-distance from a point P on one of two parallel h-lines to the other decreases as P moves in the direction of parallelism.*

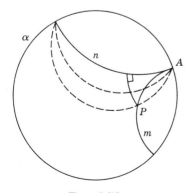

FIG. 8.78

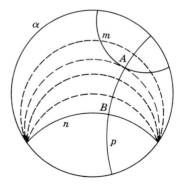

FIG. 8.79

Let m and n be the parallel h-lines and A their ideal point of tangency (Fig. 8.78). Let P be a point on m. Then as P moves toward A on m, it moves inside the system of hypercycles whose base line is n. Therefore the distance between P and n decreases and approaches zero.

     COROLLARY 2   *Two ultra-parallel h-lines have a unique common perpendicular which is the shortest h-distance from one to the other.*

Let m and n be two ultra-parallel h-lines (Fig. 8.79). Then Theorem 8.24 gives us the unique common perpendicular h-line p. Let $p \cdot m = A$ and $p \cdot n = B$; and let $h(AB) = d$. Then one branch of the hypercycle with n as base line and d as distance is tangent to m at A while hypercycles with the same base line but smaller distances do not intersect m. Note too that hypercycles with greater distances and base line n intersect m in two points, so that the distance from a point on m to n increases on either side of the common perpendicular p.

We end this section with Klein's representation of the relationship between the projective model of the hyperbolic plane (Sec. 7.3) and the Poin-

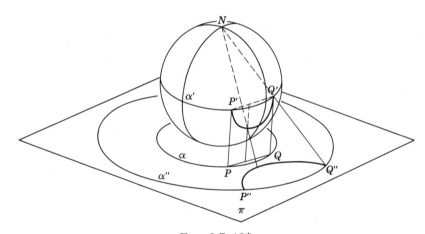

FIG. 8.7 10*

caré model. Let the projective model be the interior of circle α on plane π (Fig. 8.7 10) and let open chord PQ be an h-line in this model. By parallel projection in a direction perpendicular to π, α and its interior are projected onto the lower hemisphere of a sphere whose radius is equal to the radius

*Figure taken from Hilbert and Cohn-Vossen, *Geometry and the Imagination* (Chelsea Publishing Company, New York, 1952).

of α and which is tangent to π at the center S of α. Under this parallel projection α corresponds to the equator α' on the sphere, and line PQ corresponds to semicircular arc $P'Q'$ on the sphere meeting α' at right angles. Now by stereographic projection from the point N on the sphere diametrically opposite S, the hemisphere is projected into π. Then α' corresponds to a circle α'' concentric with α, and the semicircle $P'Q'$ corresponds to circular arc $P''Q''$ orthogonal to α''. This yields the Poincaré model of the hyperbolic plane.

Coxeter suggests that the relationship between the two models be shown by letting π be the equatorial plane of the sphere and carrying out the same two projections. This has the advantage of having the three circles α, α', and α'' identical [Coxeter (3), p. 290].

Exercises

1. In the Poincaré model represent the following: (a) a pencil of intersecting h-lines, (b) a pencil of parallel h-lines, (c) a pencil of ultra-parallel h-lines.

2. In the Poincaré model represent the following: (a) an asymptotic triangle (Sec. 1.4), (b) a doubly asymptotic triangle (two vertices ideal), (c) a triply asymptotic triangle (three ideal vertices; note that the sum of its angles is zero!).

3. In the Poincaré model prove that two h-lines perpendicular to the same h-line are ultra-parallel.

4. Prove that directed h-distance AB is the negative of directed h-distance BA, but that $h(AB) = h(BA)$.

5. Show that the subset of circular transformations which keep a given circle and its interior invariant, forms a group.

6. What does Th. 8.75 become if the two given intersecting h-lines are orthogonal?

7. Given an acute angle θ, show that there exists a unique h-distance d such that θ is the angle of parallelism for d.

8. Show that in general the h-center of an h-circle does not coincide with its Euclidean center. When are these centers identical?

9. What is the counterpart of a horocycle in the Euclidean plane? What is the counterpart of Th. 8.78 in the Euclidean plane?

10. In Fig. 8.77 show that the inversion in the circle on which m lies, transforms h-segment AB into h-segment AC.

11. Verify Hilbert's axioms for hyperbolic geometry in the Poincaré model.

12. Show that if x is the Euclidean distance of an h-point A from the center O of unit circle α, then $h(OA)$ is given by

$$d = k \ln \frac{1 + x}{1 - x}, \quad \text{and therefore} \quad x = \tanh d/2k.$$

13. Using Klein's relationship between the projective and the Poincaré model of the hyperbolic plane, show what figures in the projective model correspond to h-circles and horocycles.

14. In the Poincaré model, if α has the equation $z\bar{z} = 1$, show that the transformations $z' = (az + \bar{b})/(bz + \bar{a})$, $a\bar{a} - b\bar{b} = 1$, keep α and its interior invariant. Show they form a group.

8.8 Circular Models of the Elliptic and Euclidean Planes

In Section 1.6 it was pointed out that the double elliptic plane may be represented by the surface of a Euclidean sphere with lines defined as great circles on the sphere. The single elliptic plane, which concerns us here, may be represented by the surface of a Euclidean hemisphere with each pair of diametrically opposite points on the bounding great circle considered as a single point. Under stereographic projection of this hemisphere into an inversion plane tangent to the hemisphere and parallel to the plane of its bounding great circle, the hemisphere corresponds to the interior of a circle α and its circumference. The semi-great circles on the hemisphere correspond to arcs of "circles" through diametrically opposite points on α. This suggests the following model.

DEFINITION 8.81   Let α be a Euclidean unit circle in the inversion plane. Then the points of the elliptic plane, *e-points*, are the points of the inversion plane interior to α or on α, with the stipulation that pairs of diametrically opposite points on α are to be considered as single points of the elliptic plane. The lines of the elliptic plane, *e-lines*, are the arcs of "circles" of the inversion plane which intersect α in diametrically opposite points and which are made up of *e*-points. α is itself an *e*-line. The *e-angle* between two *e*-lines is the Euclidean angle between the "circles" on which they lie.

Since the two points in which an *e*-line meets α constitute just one *e*-point, all *e*-lines are closed curves. From the stereographic relationship between this model and the hemispherical one the following theorems are evident.

THEOREM 8.81   *Two distinct e-points determine a unique e-line.*

THEOREM 8.82   *Two distinct e-lines determine a unique e-point.*

THEOREM 8.83   *All e-lines perpendicular to a given e-line p intersect in an e-point P, and every e-line through P is perpendicular to p. P is called the* pole *of p; p is called the* polar *of P.*

To find the pole P of a given *e*-line p in our model we may proceed as follows: Let p (Fig. 8.81) intersect α in *e*-point A (which is identical with A_1). The diameter AA_1 is also an *e*-line m. Its perpendicular bisector contains an *e*-line n which is perpendicular to p. Let q be the *e*-line through A perpendicular to p. Then the point of intersection of q and n is *e*-point P, the pole of p. Note that all *e*-lines through P lie on "circles" of the inversion plane which meet again at P', the inverse of P with respect to the circle on which p lies. P' is *not* an *e*-point.

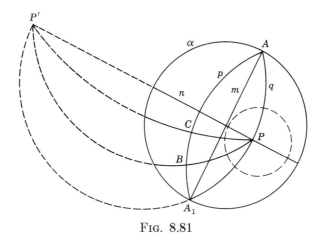

Fig. 8.81

Definition 8.82   Let B and C be two e-points (Fig. 8.81); let p be the e-line determined by them and let P be the pole of p. Then the *e-distance* BC is the radian measure of angle BPC.

Theorem 8.84   *An e-line has finite length π.*

Since e-distance is given in terms of angles between "circles," and since these angles are invariant under stereographic projection, equal distances on the sphere correspond to equal e-distances in the model.

Definition 8.83   The locus of e-points a given e-distance d, $0 < d < \pi$, from a given e-point, is called an *e-circle.*

Since a circle on the sphere cuts all great circles through its center orthogonally, an e-circle will cut all e-lines through its center orthogonally. Hence an e-circle with e-center P (Fig. 8.81) is part of a "circle" of the inversion plane which belongs to the coaxal set of Type II orthogonal to the set determined by circles through P and P'. An e-circle may consist of parts of a pair of such circles, as is illustrated in Fig. 8.82. Let β be an e-circle with e-center P and radius d small enough so that β is entirely inside α. As d gets larger, β will become a circle tangent to α at point A (which is identical with A_1). As d gets still larger the circle of which β is a part will intersect α in two points B and C, which are identical with B_1 and C_1, their diametrically opposite points on α. B_1 and C_1 lie on another circle of the coaxal system of Type II. β will then consist of the pair of arcs BC and B_1C_1, which form *one* e-circle.

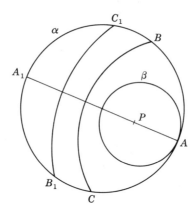

FIG. 8.82

It is beyond the scope of this book to pursue elliptic geometry further. It is of interest to note, however, that this model satisfies the axioms of Sec. 3.2 and hence that the real elliptic plane is a projective plane. This may also be seen by noting that we may project the Euclidean hemisphere onto a projective plane tangent to the hemisphere and parallel to the plane of its bounding great circle, by using the center O of the sphere as center of projection. Such a projection is called a *gnomonic projection* (cf. Ex. 3 of Sec. 3.7). Under a gnomonic projection the semi-great circles on the hemisphere correspond to lines in the projective plane with the bounding great circle corresponding to l_∞. We introduce a metric, to get the elliptic plane, by defining the distance between two points A, B on the plane as the radian measure of $\sphericalangle AOB$; and we define the angle between two lines m, n on the plane as the angle between the planes determined by O, m and O, n.

We have exhibited models of the hyperbolic and elliptic planes in which h-lines and e-lines were "circles" of the inversion plane. We close this section by indicating how the same thing can be done for the Euclidean plane.

Consider the Euclidean plane as embedded in an inversion plane and perform an inversion with any point $P \neq P_\infty$ as center. Then all the lines of the Euclidean plane are transformed into "circles" of the inversion plane all going through P, and P itself is transformed into P_∞. This suggests the following model.

DEFINITION 8.84   Let π be an inversion plane. Then the *E-points* are the points of π with the exception of a fixed point $P \neq P_\infty$. The *E-lines* are "circles" of the inversion plane which go through P. P is not on the E-line (cf. Ex. 8 of Sec. 2.10).

Then by suitable definitions suggested by the inversion from which our model is derived, it can be shown that this model satisfies Hilbert's axioms for a Euclidean plane. For example, if we define parallel E-lines as "circles" of the inversion plane tangent to each other at P, then Theorem 8.23 shows that through a given E-point A not on a given E-line m there exists one and only one E-line parallel to m.

Exercises

1. (a) Find the polar e-line of a given e-point P. (b) Where is the pole of e-line α?

2. Show that the e-distance from any e-point to any point on its polar is $\pi/2$ (use Fig. 8.81).

3. (a) What is an e-circle whose radius is $\pi/2$? (b) Is an e-circle ever part of a Euclidean line?

4. What are the counterparts of hypercycles in the elliptic plane?

5. Show that two e-circles may intersect in four e-points.

6. The transformation $T(P) = P'$ such that $OP \cdot OP' = -r^2$, where O is the center of a circle of radius r and where O, P, P' are collinear, is called an anti-inversion. It is equivalent to the product of an inversion in the circle and a reflection in the center of inversion O. Show that under this transformation, a circle which cuts the circle of inversion in diametrically opposite points is invariant.

7. In Fig. 8.81 show that all e-lines through P lie on "circles" of the inversion plane which meet again at P', the inverse of P with respect to p; and show that P and P' are anti-inverse (Ex. 6 above) with respect to α.

8. In the model of Def. 8.84 prove that through a given E-point one and only one perpendicular can be drawn to a given E-line.

8.9 Summary: Transformation Groups and Their Associated Geometries

We have applied Klein's classification of geometries to those characterized by groups of linear transformations and circular transformations. We found that Euclidean geometry, far from being the only possible geometry, was one of many subgeometries of other "larger" geometries.

To summarize: Let S be a set of points P such that a unique point P corresponds to an ordered pair of real numbers (x, y), and let S' (which may be S) be a set of points $P'(x', y')$. Let a one-to-one correspondence between points P and P' be given by the transformations $x' = f(x, y)$, $y' = g(x, y)$. If a set of these transformations forms a group then the properties of the associated geometry are determined by the functions f and g. For example, if f and g are linear functions we get affine geometry or similarity geometry, etc., depending on the particular group of linear functions formed.

As we generalize the functions f and g we get larger groups, each leading to another area of study. If the group of transformations consists of all the rational functions f and g such that the inverse transformations are also rational and if these functions are continuous, the associated geometry is called *Algebraic Geometry*. If we drop the requirement of rationality in this set of transformations, we obtain *Topology*. The study of each geometry consists of a search for properties invariant under the corresponding group of transformations.

The converse problem is also of considerable interest—that of finding transformations of one set of points onto another so that certain pre-assigned properties are preserved. One of the oldest problems of this type has its origin in the attempts to draw a map of the earth (or part of it) on a sheet of paper. This is essentially the problem of finding a transformation of all or part of the surface of a sphere onto a finite section of a plane with the least possible distortion of figures. It is impossible to find such a transformation that will preserve *all* desirable properties such as equality of areas, distances, and angle measures. However, there are different transformations for different purposes. For example, stereographic projection preserves angle measure, gnomonic projection preserves geodesics (the shortest distance path between two points on the sphere corresponds to that on the plane; i.e., a great circle on the sphere corresponds to a straight line on the plane). For an excellent discussion of map-projections the reader is referred to W. Chamberlin's *The Round Earth on Flat Paper*, published by the National Geographic Society.

As stated in the preface, the purpose of this book was to make the student aware of new roads to geometry. A few signposts have been set up, therefore, with the hope that students will be led to browse in new fields and that some of the more hardy ones will push ahead to extend the roads to still newer fields.

References

Adler, Chaps. 5, 14; Courant and Robbins, Chap. III, Secs. 4, 6; Coxeter (3), Chap. 6; Eves, Secs. 3.4, 3.7, 8.4, 12.5. 12.6; Graustein, Chap. XVIII; Hilbert and Cohn-Vossen, Secs. 36, 37; Kutuzov, Chap. VIII, and Secs. 17, 79; Wolfe, Chap. VIII and App. III, IV.

APPENDIX

AXIOM SETS FOR
EUCLIDEAN GEOMETRY

Appendix 1 Euclid's Definitions, Postulates, and the First Thirty Propositions of Book I*

DEFINITIONS

1. A point is that which has no part.
2. A line is breadthless length.
3. The extremities of a line are points.
4. A straight line is a line which lies evenly with the points on itself.
5. A surface is that which has length and breadth only.
6. The extremities of a surface are lines.
7. A plane surface is a surface which lies evenly with the straight lines on itself.
8. A plane angle is the inclination to one another of two lines in a plane which meet one another and do not lie in a straight line.
9. And when the lines containing the angle are straight, the angle is called rectilineal.
10. When a straight line set up on a straight line makes the adjacent angles equal to one another, each of the equal angles is right, and the straight line standing on the other is called perpendicular to that on which it stands.
11. An obtuse angle is an angle greater than a right angle.
12. An acute angle is an angle less than a right angle.
13. A boundary is that which is an extremity of anything.
14. A figure is that which is contained by any boundary or boundaries.
15. A circle is a plane figure contained by one line such that all the straight lines falling upon it from one point among those lying within the figure are equal to one another.
16. And the point is called the centre of the circle.

*Appendix 1 reprinted from Sir Thomas L. Heath, *The Thirteen Books of Euclid's Elements*, by permission of the Cambridge University Press, publishers.

179

17. A diameter of the circle is any straight line drawn through the cen're and terminated in both directions by the circumference of the circle, and such a straight line also bisects the circle.

18. A semicircle is the figure contained by the diameter and the circumference cut off by it. And the centre of the semicircle is the same as that of the circle.

19. Rectilineal figures are those which are contained by straight lines, trilateral figures being those contained by three, quadrilateral those contained by four, and multilateral those contained by more than four straight lines.

20. Of trilateral figures, an equilateral triangle is that which has three sides equal, an isosceles triangle that which has two of its sides alone equal, and a scalene triangle that which has its three sides unequal.

21. Further, of trilateral figures, a right-angled triangle is that which has a right angle, an obtuse-angled triangle that which has an obtuse angle, and an acute-angled triangle that which has its three angles acute.

22. Of quadrilateral figures, a square is that which is both equilateral and right-angled; an oblong that which is right-angled but not equilateral; a rhombus that which is equilateral but not right-angled; and a rhomboid that which has its opposite sides and angles equal to one another but is neither equilateral nor right-angled. And let quadrilaterals other than these be called trapezia.

23. Parallel straight lines are straight lines which, being in the same plane and being produced indefinitely in both directions, do not meet one another in either direction.

THE POSTULATES

1. To draw a straight line from any point to any point.
2. To produce a finite straight line continuously in a straight line.
3. To describe a circle with any centre and distance.
4. That all right angles are equal to one another.
5. That, if a straight line falling on two straight lines make the interior angles on the same side less than two right angles, the two straight lines, if produced indefinitely, meet on that side on which are the angles less than the two right angles.

THE COMMON NOTIONS

1. Things which are equal to the same thing are also equal to one another.
2. If equals be added to equals, the wholes are equal.
3. If equals be subtracted from equals, the remainders are equal.
4. Things which coincide with one another are equal to one another.
5. The whole is greater than the part.

THE FIRST THIRTY PROPOSITIONS OF BOOK I

1. On a given finite straight line, to construct an equilateral triangle.
2. To place at a given point (as an extremity) a straight line equal to a given straight line.
3. Given two unequal straight lines, to cut off from the greater a straight line equal to the less.
4. If two triangles have the two sides equal to two sides respectively, and have the angles contained by the equal straight lines equal, they will also have the base equal to the base, the triangle will be equal to the triangle, and the remaining angles will be equal to the remaining angles respectively, namely, those which the equal sides subtend.
5. In isosceles triangles, the angles at the base are equal to one another, and, if the equal straight lines be produced further, the angles under the base will be equal to one another.
6. If in a triangle two angles be equal to one another, the sides which subtend the equal angles will also be equal to one another.
7. Given two straight lines constructed on a straight line (from its extremities) and meeting in a point, there cannot be constructed on the same straight line (from its extremities), and on the same side of it, two other straight lines meeting in another point and equal to the former two respectively, namely, each to that which has the same extremity with it.
8. If two triangles have the two sides equal to two sides respectively, and have also the base equal to the base, they will also have the angles equal which are contained by the equal straight lines.
9. To bisect a given rectilineal angle.
10. To bisect a given finite straight line.
11. To draw a straight line at right angles to a given straight line from a given point on it.
12. To a given infinite straight line, from a given point which is not on it, to draw a perpendicular straight line.
13. If a straight line set up on a straight line make angles, it will make either two right angles or angles equal to two right angles.
14. If with any straight line, and at a point on it, two straight lines not lying on the same side make the adjacent angles equal to two right angles, the two straight lines will be in a straight line with one another.
15. If two straight lines cut one another, they make the vertical angles equal to one another.
16. In any triangle if one of the sides be produced, the exterior angle is greater than either of the interior and opposite angles.
17. In any triangle two angles taken together in any manner are less than two right angles.
18. In any triangle the greater side subtends the greater angle.

19. In any triangle the greater angle is subtended by the greater side.

20. In any triangle two sides taken together in any manner are greater than the remaining one.

21. If on one of the sides of a triangle, from its extremities, there be constructed two straight lines meeting within the triangle, the straight lines so constructed will be less than the remaining two sides of the triangle, but will contain a greater angle.

22. Out of three straight lines, which are equal to three given straight lines, to construct a triangle: thus it is necessary that two of the straight lines taken together in any manner should be greater than the remaining one.

23. On a given straight line and at a point on it, to construct a rectilineal angle equal to a given rectilineal angle.

24. If two triangles have the two sides equal to two sides respectively, but have the one of the angles contained by the equal straight lines greater than the other, they will also have the base greater than the base.

25. If two triangles have the two sides equal to two sides respectively, but have the base greater than the base, they will also have the one of the angles contained by the equal straight lines greater than the other.

26. If two triangles have the two angles equal to two angles respectively, and one side equal to one side, namely, either the side adjoining the equal angles, or that subtending one of the equal angles, they will also have the remaining sides equal to the remaining sides and the remaining angle to the remaining angle.

27. If a straight line falling on two straight lines make the alternate angles equal to one another, the straight lines will be parallel to one another.

28. If a straight line falling on two straight lines make the exterior angle equal to the interior and opposite angle on the same side, or the interior angles on the same side equal to two right angles, the straight lines will be parallel to one another.

29. A straight line falling on parallel straight lines makes the alternate angles equal to one another, the exterior angle equal to the interior and opposite angle, and the interior angles on the same side equal to two right angles.

30. Straight lines parallel to the same straight line are also parallel to one another.

Appendix 2   Hilbert's Axioms for Euclidean Plane Geometry*

GROUP I   *Axioms of Connection*

I–1. Through any two distinct points A, B, there is always a line m.

*Appendix 2 translated from D. Hilbert, *Grundlagen der Geometrie* (1962) by permission of the Open Court Publishing Co.

I–2. Through any two distinct points A, B, there is not more than one line m.

I–3. On every line there exist at least two distinct points. There exist at least three points which are not on the same line.

I–4. Through any three points, not on the same line, there is one and only one plane.

GROUP II   *Axioms of Order*

II–1. If point B is between points A and C, then A, B, C are distinct points on the same line, and B is between C and A.

II–2. For any two distinct points A and C, there is at least one point B on the line AC such that C is between A and B.

II–3. If A, B, C are three distinct points on the same line, then only one of the points is between the other two.

> DEFINITION   By the *segment AB* is meant the set of all points which are between A and B. Points A and B are called the *end points* of the segment. The segment AB is the same as segment BA.

II–4. (Pasch's Axiom) Let A, B, C be three points not on the same line and let m be a line in the plane A, B, C, which does not pass through any of the points A, B, C. Then if m passes through a point of the segment AB, it will also pass through a point of segment AC or a point of segment BC.

Note:

II–4′. This postulate may be replaced by the *Separation Axiom:* A line m separates the points of the plane which are not on m, into two sets such that if two points X and Y are in the same set, the segment XY does not intersect m, and if X and Y are in different sets, the segment XY does intersect m. In the first case X and Y are said to be on same side of m; in the second case, X and Y are said to be on opposite sides of m.

> DEFINITION   By the *ray AB* is meant the set of points consisting of those which are between A and B, the point B itself, and all points C such that B is between A and C. The ray AB is said to *emanate from* point A.

> A point A, on a given line m, divides m into two rays such that two points are on the same ray if and only if A is not between them.

> DEFINITION   If A, B, C are three points not on the same line, then the system of three segments AB, BC, CA and their endpoints is called the *triangle ABC*. The three segments are called the *sides* of the triangle, and the three points are called the *vertices*.

GROUP III　*Axioms of Congruence*

III–1. If A and B are distinct points on line m, and if A' is a point on line m' (not necessarily distinct from m), then there is one and only one point B' on each ray of m' emanating from A' such that the segment $A'B'$ is congruent to the segment AB.

III–2. If two segments are each congruent to a third, then they are congruent to each other.

(From this it can be shown that congruence of segments is an equivalence relation; i.e., $AB \cong AB$; if $AB \cong A'B'$, then $A'B' \cong AB$; and if $AB \cong CD$ and $CD \cong EF$, then $AB \cong EF$.)

III–3. If point C is between A and B, and point C' is between A' and B', and if the segment $AC \cong$ segment $A'C'$, and the segment $CB \cong$ segment $C'B'$, then segment $AB \cong$ segment $A'B'$.

DEFINITION　By an *angle* is meant a point (called the *vertex* of the angle) and two rays (called the *sides* of the angle) emanating from the point.

If the vertex of the angle is point A and if B and C are any two points other than A on the two sides of the angle, we speak of the angle BAC or CAB or simply of angle A.

III–4. If BAC is an angle whose sides do not lie on the same line and if in a given plane, $A'B'$ is a ray emanating from A', then there is one and only one ray $A'C'$ on a given side of line $A'B'$, such that $\angle B'A'C' \cong \angle BAC$. In short, a given angle in a given plane can be laid off on a given side of a given ray in one and only one way. Every angle is congruent to itself.

DEFINITION　If ABC is a triangle then the three angles BAC, CBA, and ACB are called the angles of the triangle. Angle BAC is said to be *included* by the sides AB and AC of the triangle.

III–5. If two sides and the included angle of one triangle are congruent respectively to two sides and the included angle of another triangle, then each of the remaining angles of the first triangle is congruent to the corresponding angle of the second triangle.

GROUP IV　*Axiom of Parallels (for a plane)*

IV–1. (Playfair's postulate) Through a given point A not on a given line m there passes at most one line, which does not intersect m.

GROUP V   *Axioms of Continuity*

V–1. (Axiom of measure or the Archimedean axiom) If AB and CD are arbitrary segments, then there exists a number n such that if segment CD is laid off n times on the ray AB starting from A, then a point E is reached, where $n \cdot CD = AE$, and where B is between A and E.

V–2. (Axiom of linear completeness) The system of points on a line with its order and congruence relations cannot be extended in such a way that the relations existing among its elements as well as the basic properties of linear order and congruence resulting from the Axioms I–III, and V–1 remain valid.

Note:

    V′. These axioms may be replaced by *Dedekind's axiom of continuity:* For every partition of the points on a line into two non-empty sets such that no point of either lies between two points of the other, there is a point of one set which lies between every other point of that set and every point of the other set.

Appendix 3   Birkhoff's Postulates for Euclidean Plane Geometry[*]

UNDEFINED ELEMENTS AND RELATIONS: (a) *points,* $A, B, \cdots$; (b) sets of points called *lines,* $m, n, \cdots$; (c) *distance* between any two points: $d(A, B)$ a real non-negative number with $d(A, B) = d(B, A)$; (d) *angle* formed by three ordered points $A, O, B, (A \neq O, B \neq O)$: $\sphericalangle AOB$, a real number (mod 2π). The point O is called the vertex of the angle.

POSTULATE I   *Postulate of line measure:* The points $A, B, \cdots$ of any line m can be put into $1:1$ correspondence with the real numbers x so that $|x_B - x_A| = d(A, B)$ for all points A, B.

DEFINITIONS   A point B is *between* A and C $(A \neq C)$ if $d(A, B) + d(B, C) = d(A, C)$. The points A and C together with all points B between A and C form *segment AC.* The *half-line m'* with *endpoint O* is defined by two points O, A in line m $(A \neq O)$ as the set of all points A' of m such that O is not between A and A'. If A, B, C are three distinct points the three segments AB, BC, CA are said to form a *triangle ABC* with *sides AB, BC, CA* and *vertices A, B, C.* If A, B, C are in the same line, $\triangle ABC$ is said to be *degenerate.*

POSTULATE II   *Point–line postulate:* One and only one line m contains two given points P, Q $(P \neq Q)$. If two distinct lines have no points in common they are *parallel.* A line is always regarded as parallel to itself.

*Appendix 3 reprinted from G. D. Birkhoff, "A Set of Postulates for Plane Geometry (based on scale and protractor)," *Annals of Mathematics,* Vol. 33, 1932, by permission of the *Annals of Mathematics.*

PostULATE III *Postulate of angle measure:* The half-lines m, n, $\cdots$ thru any point O can be put into $1 : 1$ correspondence with the real numbers a (mod 2π) so that if $A \neq O$ and $B \neq O$ are points of m and n, respectively, the difference $a_n - a_m$ (mod 2π) is $\sphericalangle AOB$.

Definitions Two half-lines m, n thru O are said to form a *straight* $\sphericalangle$ if $\sphericalangle mOn = \pi$. Two half-lines m, n thru O are said to form a *right* $\sphericalangle$ if $\sphericalangle mOn = \pm \pi/2$, in which case we also say that m is *perpendicular* to n.

PostULATE IV *Postulate of similarity:* If in two triangles ABC and $A'B'C'$ and for some constant $k > 0$, $d(A', B') = kd(A, B)$, $d(A', C') = kd(A, C)$ and also $\sphericalangle B'A'C' = \pm \sphericalangle BAC$, then also $d(B', C') = kd(BC)$, $\sphericalangle C'B'A' = \pm \sphericalangle CBA$, and $\sphericalangle A'C'B' = \pm \sphericalangle ACB$.

Definitions Any two geometric figures are *similar* if there exists a $1 : 1$ correspondence between the points of the two figures such that all corresponding distances are in proportion and corresponding angles are either equal or all negatives of each other. Any two geometric figures are *congruent* if they are similar with $k = 1$.

Appendix 4   The SMSG Postulates for Euclidean Geometry*

Undefined Terms: point, line, plane.

PostULATE 1 Given any two different points, there is exactly one line which contains both of them.

PostULATE 2 *The Distance Postulate:* To every pair of different points there corresponds a unique positive number.

PostULATE 3 *The Ruler Postulate:* The points of a line can be placed in correspondence with the real numbers in such a way that
   (1) To every point of the line there corresponds exactly one real number.
   (2) To every real number there corresponds exactly one point of the line.
   (3) The distance between two points is the absolute value of the difference of the corresponding numbers.

PostULATE 4 *The Ruler Placement Postulate:* Given two points P and Q of a line, the coordinate system can be chosen in such a way that the coordinate of P is zero and the coordinate of Q is positive.

*Appendix 4 reprinted from *School Mathematics Study Group: Geometry*, by permission of the Yale University Press, 1961.

POSTULATE 5   (a) Every plane contains at least three non-collinear points. (b) Space contains at least four non-coplanar points.

POSTULATE 6   If two points lie in a plane, then the line containing these points lies in the same plane.

POSTULATE 7   Any three points lie in at least one plane, and any three non-collinear points lie in exactly one plane. More briefly, any three points are coplanar, and any three non-collinear points determine a plane.

POSTULATE 8   If two different planes intersect, then their intersection is a line.

POSTULATE 9   *The Plane Separation Postulate:* Given a line and a plane containing it, the points of the plane that do not lie on the line form two sets such that
(1) each of the sets is convex and
(2) if P is in one set and Q is in the other then the segment $\overline{PQ}$ intersects the line.

POSTULATE 10   *The Space Separation Postulate:* The points of space that do not lie in a given plane form two sets such that
(1) each of the sets is convex and
(2) if P is in one set and Q is in the other then the segment $\overline{PQ}$ intersects the plane.

POSTULATE 11   *The Angle Measurement Postulate:* To every angle $\angle BAC$ there corresponds a real number between 0 and 180.

POSTULATE 12   *The Angle Construction Postulate:* Let $\overrightarrow{AB}$ be a ray on the edge of the half-plane H. For every number r between 0 and 180 there is exactly one ray $\overrightarrow{AP}$, with P in H, such that $m \angle PAB = r$.

POSTULATE 13   *The Angle Addition Postulate:* If D is a point in the interior of $\angle BAC$, then $m \angle BAC = m \angle BAD + m \angle DAC$.

POSTULATE 14   *The Supplement Postulate:* If two angles form a linear pair, then they are supplementary.

POSTULATE 15   *The S.A.S. Postulate:* Given a correspondence between two triangles (or between a triangle and itself). If two sides and the included angle of the first triangle are congruent to the corresponding parts of the second triangle, then the correspondence is a congruence.

POSTULATE 16   *The Parallel Postulate:* Through a given external point there is at most one line parallel to a given line.

POSTULATE 17   To every polygonal region there corresponds a unique positive number.

POSTULATE 18   If two triangles are congruent, then the triangular regions have the same area.

POSTULATE 19   Suppose that the region R is the union of two regions R_1 and R_2. Suppose that R_1 and R_2 intersect at most in a finite number of segments and points. Then the area of R is the sum of the areas of R_1 and R_2.

POSTULATE 20   The area of a rectangle is the product of the length of its base and the length of its altitude.

POSTULATE 21   The volume of a rectangular parallelpiped is the product of the altitude and the area of the base.

POSTULATE 22   *Cavalieri's Principle:* Given two solids and a plane. If for every plane which intersects the solids and is parallel to the given plane the two intersections have equal areas, then the two solids have the same volume.

BIBLIOGRAPHY

Adler, C. F., *Modern Geometry* (McGraw-Hill Book Co., Inc., New York, 1958).

Blumenthal, L. M., *A Modern View of Geometry* (W. H. Freeman and Co., San Francisco, 1961).

Bonola, R., *Non-Euclidean Geometry* (Dover Publications, Inc., New York, 1955).

Busemann, H., and Kelly, P. J., *Projective Geometry and Projective Metrics* (Academic Press Inc., New York, 1953).

Courant, R., and Robbins, H., *What is Mathematics?* (Oxford University Press, New York, 1941).

Coxeter, H. S. M. (1), *The Real Projective Plane* (McGraw-Hill Book Co., Inc., New York, 1959); (2) *Contributions of Geometry to the Mainstream of Mathematics* (Oklahoma A & M College, 1955); (3) *Introduction to Geometry* (John Wiley & Sons, Inc., New York, 1961).

Eves, H., *A Survey of Geometry*, Vol. I & II (Allyn and Bacon, Inc., Boston, Massachusetts, 1963, 1965).

Eves, H., and Newsom, C. V., *An Introduction to the Foundations and Fundamental Concepts of Mathematics* (Holt, Rinehart and Winston, Inc., New York, 1958).

Faulkner, T. E., *Projective Geometry* (Interscience Publishers, Inc., New York, 1952).

Fishback, W. T., *Projective and Euclidean Geometry* (John Wiley & Sons, Inc., New York, 1962).

Forder, H. G., *Foundations of Euclidean Geometry* (Dover Publications, Inc., New York, 1958).

Graustein, W. C., *Introduction to Higher Geometry* (The Macmillan Co., New York, 1933).

Heath, T. L., *Euclid's Elements*, Vol. I (Dover Publications, Inc., New York, 1956).

Hilbert, D., *The Foundations of Geometry* (Open Court Publishing Co., LaSalle, Illinois, 1902).

Hilbert, D., and Cohn-Vossen, S., *Geometry and the Imagination* (Chelsea Publishing Co., New York, 1952).

Klein, F., *Elementary Mathematics from an Advanced Standpoint: Geometry* (Dover Publications, Inc., New York, 1945).

Kutuzov, B. V., *Geometry*, Vol. IV of Studies in Mathematics (SMSG Publications, A. C. Vroman, Pasadena, California, 1960).

Levi, H., *Foundations of Geometry and Trigonometry* (Prentice-Hall, Inc., Englewood Cliffs, New Jersey, 1960).

Levy, H., *Projective and Related Geometries* (The Macmillan Co., New York, 1964).

Meserve, B. E., *Fundamental Concepts of Geometry* (Addison-Wesley Publishing Co., Inc., Reading, Massachusetts, 1955).

Moise, E., *Elementary Geometry from an Advanced Standpoint* (Addison-Wesley Publishing Co., Inc., Reading, Massachusetts, 1963).

Prenowitz, W., and Jordan, M., *Basic Concepts of Geometry* (Blaisdell Publishing Co., New York, 1965).

Robinson, G. de B., *The Foundations of Geometry* (Toronto Press, 1946).

Seidenberg, A., *Lectures in Projective Geometry* (D. Van Nostrand Co., Inc., Princeton, New Jersey, 1962).

Stabler, E. R., *Introduction to Mathematical Thought* (Addison-Wesley Publishing Co., Inc., Reading, Massachusetts, 1953).

Struik, D. J., *Lectures on Analytic and Projective Geometry* (Addison-Wesley Publishing Co., Inc., Reading, Massachusetts, 1953).

Wilder, R. L., *Introduction to the Foundations of Mathematics* (John Wiley & Sons, Inc., 1952).

Wolfe, H. E., *Introduction to Non-Euclidean Geometry* (Dryden Press, Inc., New York, 1945).

Woods, F. S., *Higher Geometry* (Dover Publications, Inc., New York, 1961).

Young, J. W. (1), *Lectures on Fundamental Concepts of Algebra and Geometry* (The Macmillan Co., Inc., New York, 1936); (2) *Projective Geometry*, Carus Monograph 4 (Open Court Publishing Co., LaSalle, Illinois, 1930).

Young, J. W. A., *Monographs on Topics of Modern Mathematics* (Dover Publications, Inc., New York, 1955).

Twenty-third Yearbook, *Insights into Modern Mathematics* (National Council of Teachers of Mathematics, 1957).

School Mathematics Study Group Publications in Geometry (A. C. Vroman, Pasadena, California, 1959–1961).

ANSWERS TO SELECTED EXERCISES

Sec. 1.2
2. Parallel lines are everywhere equidistant.

Sec. 1.5
5. Let D be any point on side AC of triangle ABC. Then the sum of the angles of triangle ABD equals the sum of the angles of triangle BDC equals the sum of the angles of triangle ABC equals k. A little elementary algebraic manipulation yields the desired result.

8. Draw perpendiculars from the vertices of the quadrilateral to the base line and use the properties of the Saccheri quadrilaterals thus formed.

Sec. 2.3
4. Use Axioms I–3, I–1, II–2, and II–4 to obtain the accompanying figure and the required proof.

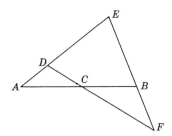

Sec. 2.9
2. All independent.

3. All independent.

4. (b) and (c) not independent.

Sec. 2.10
5. Axioms of connection and order are valid; axiom of parallelism not valid.

6, 7, 8, 9. Axioms of connection, order and parallelism are all valid.

Sec. 3.3
5. Use Desargues' axiom on triangle ABC and triangle $A'B'C'$.

Sec. 3.4
3. Solution is unique [see Coxeter (1), p. 15].

Sec. 3.5

6. $ABD \overset{C}{\underset{\wedge}{=}} GFD \overset{E}{\underset{\wedge}{=}} BAD$ making $ABD \overline{\wedge} BAD$.

Sec. 3.8

6. Use Pappus' Theorem on hexagon $A_1A_2CB_1B_2D$.

Sec. 3.9

2. Use fact that $AA, AC, AD, AE \overline{\wedge} BA, BC, BD, BE$ and proceed as in proof of Theorem 3.91.

Sec. 4.1

5. No.

6. (a) $x' = -(y + 2)$, $y' = x - 3$
   (c) $x' = x + 3$, $y' = y - 2$
   (e) $x' = x - 6$, $y' = y + 4$

7. (a) $x' = 7x - 2y$, $y = -3y$

   (c) $x' = \dfrac{(x + y)}{3}$, $y' = \dfrac{(2y - x)}{3}$

Sec. 5.1

6. $(2, 8, 17)$

9. $(0, x - y, x - 1)$, $(y - x, 0, y - 1)$, $(1 - x, 1 - y, 0)$

12. $R = (1, -1, 0)$, $S = (1, 0, -1)$, $T = (0, 1, -1)$.
    Line $RST = [1, 1, 1]$

14. (a) $(2, -1)$

Sec. 5.2

5. $\delta x_1' = -x_2$, $\delta x_2' = x_1 - x_2$

7. $\delta x_1' = 6x_1 - 4x_2$, $\delta x_2' = x_1 + x_2$

Sec. 5.3

5. (a) $(1, 2)$
   (c) $(5, 4)$

9. $(6, 1, -1)$

11. $R(5, 7, 1, 3)$, etc.

Sec. 5.4

3. (a) $(2, 1)$ and $(3, 1)$
   (c) none
   (e) $(0, 1)$

9. $\delta x_1' = 2x_1 + x_2$, $\delta x_2' = -x_1 - 2x_2$

11. $\delta x_1' = 10x_1 - 12x_2$, $\delta x_2' = 3x_1 - 2x_2$

17. No.

19. The involution is $\delta x_1' = 3x_1 + 2x_2$, $\delta x_2' = -3x_1 - 3x_2$

Sec. 5.5

5. $\delta x_1' = x_1 + 2x_2 - 2x_3$, $\delta x_2' = 2x_1 + 2x_2 - 2x_3$, $\delta x_3' = x_2$

7. $\delta x_1' = x_1 - x_2 + x_3$, $\delta x_2' = x_1 - 2x_2 + 2x_3$, $\delta x_3' = 2x_1 - 4x_2 + 3x_3$

9. (a) $(1, 0, 0)$, $(0, 0, 1)$, $[0, 1, 0]$, $[0, 0, 1]$
   (c) $(1, 0 ,0)$, $[0, 0, 1]$

Sec. 5.6
1. (a) $2x_1^2 + x_2^2 - 2x_1x_3 + 2x_2x_3 = 0$,
   $u_1^2 + u_2^2 - 2u_3^2 + 2u_1u_2 - 2u_1u_3 + 4u_2u_3 = 0$
3. $[3, -1, 3]$
8. $(3, -3, 1)$
19. Use the reference triangle as triangle ABC and hence the conic of Exercise 11.

Sec. 6.1
4. $x' = 5x + 2y$, $y' = x - 3y$

Sec. 6.2
11. $(a + b, 2)$

Sec. 6.3
6. (a) Ellipse with center $(0, 0, 1)$
   (c) Ellipse with center $(3, -2, 1)$
   (e) Ellipse with center $(0, 0, 1)$
   (g) Hyperbola with center $(0, 0, 1)$, with asymptotes $[1, 1, 0]$ and $[1, -1, 0]$

Sec. 6.4
6. Exception when $b = 0$ and $a = 1$
10. $x' = y + 6$, $y' = -x + 6$; $x' = x - 3$, $y' = -(y + 3)$

Sec. 6.6
3. (a) $|x| + |y| = 1$ which is the square whose vertices are $(1, 0)$, $(0, 1)$, $(-1, 0)$ and $(0, -1)$

Sec. 6.7
8. $x' = 3x/5 + 4y/5 - 2/5$, $y' = -4x/5 + 3y/5 + 6/5$
10. Use a translation T such that $T(A) = D$, followed by a rotation with center D.

Sec 7.1
1. $[1, 1, -1]$
7. $(1, -3, -1)$
10. $(i, 1, 2 + i)$ and $(-i, 1, 2 - i)$

Sec. 7.4
4. $k\pi/2$

Sec. 8.1
3. (a) A pencil of "circles" tangent at center of inversion
   (c) A circle concentric to circle of inversion.
8. No.
11. Let B be the inverse of A in α. Then any circle β with B as center is the required circle.
13. Use $(0, 0)$ as the center of the two circles and do the problem analytically.

Sec. 8.2
5. Use given circle as circle of inversion.

Sec. 8.3

    5. Invert α and β into two concentric circles.

Sec. 8.4

    3. (a) ± 1

        (c) $-\frac{1}{2} \pm i\sqrt{3}/2$

INDEX

Absolute conic, 136ff., 138, 142
Absolute points, 137
Absolute unit of length, 9
Affine geometry, 104ff., 177
Affine plane, 104ff., 109, 129, 137
  congruence in, 107
  conics in, 110ff.
  parallelism in, 106
Affine transformation, 104ff., 113, 157, 160
  group, 104, 105, 114
  invariants of, 105, 106, 107, 108
Algebraic geometry, 178
Angle(s), 179, 184, 185
  congruence of, 25, 34, 118, 119
  elliptic measure of, 142, 143, 174, 176
  Euclidean measure of, 24, 117, 118, 148, 149, 186, 187
  exterior angle theorem, 14, 22
  hyperbolic measure of, 139, 143, 166
  interior of, 19, 22
  of parallelism, 6ff., 166, 173
  projective measure of, 131, 134, 137, 143
Angular region, 49
Anti-inversion, 177
Archimedean axiom, 185
Argand diagram, 158, 165
Asymptote, 111, 113
Asymptotic triangle, 7ff., 141, 173
Axiom set, 19ff.
  abstract, 26ff.
  Birkhoff's, 23, 185
  Euclid's, 3, 4, 5, 179
  Hilbert's, 21, 182
  for the projective plane, 34ff., 72ff.
  properties of, 27ff.
  SMSG, 24, 186

Axioms (*see* Congruence, Continuity, Incidence, Order, Parallelism, Separation)

Beltrami, E., 27
Betweenness, 21, 23, 33, 47, 52, 107, 110, 183, 185
Birkhoff, G. D., 21, 23, 24, 185
Bolyai, J., 5, 17
Brianchon, C. J., 35, 59

Categoricalness, 28, 32
Cayley, A., 136
Characteristic polynomial, 93
Characteristic values, 93
Circle(s)
  coaxal, 153ff., 162, 169, 175
  concentric, 151, 155, 156, 158
  in the elliptic plane, 175, 177
  in the Euclidean plane, 133, 179
  in the hyperbolic plane, 169, 173
  inverse of, 147
  of inversion, 145
  of the inversion plane, 147ff., 165, 174, 176
  orthogonal, 148, 154ff., 162, 165, 169, 175
  tangent, 152, 153, 155, 156
Circular points at infinity, 132, 133
Circular transformations, 145ff., 157ff., 177
  analytic form of, 158ff.
  group of, 159, 173
  invariants of, 160, 161, 162, 167
Coaxal circles, 153ff., 162, 169, 175
Collinearity, 34, 35, 73, 92, 102
Collineation, 90ff., 105, 136, 138, 157
  group, 91, 92, 104
  identity, 91, 92